Personal Help for Boys

Companion Workbook

From PEARABLES

This book is dedicated to all the young men of today who will soon grow to be tomorrow's men of God.

PEARABLES
Copyright 1995, Revised 2002
www.pearables.com
P.O. Box 272000
Fort Collins, CO 80527

Introduction

PERSONAL HELP FOR BOYS has been a project that we have delighted in producing. We believe every homeschooling boy should study and read this book as many times as possible, along with the companion workbook which reveals all the scriptures for principles implicated. This is a partial republication of a work written by Thomas W. Shannon. We have reformatted, edited and added as we believed would best benefit those Christian boys whose delight is in serving the Lord Jesus Christ.

The boys of today are to be the men of tomorrow. The character of the men of the future will be determined by the habits and ideals of the boys of the present generation in Christ.

Apart from the vital personal talks to boys concerning their mental, moral and physical well-being, the talks and the essays on character building will furnish every boy with valuable hints, helps and suggestions toward living up to Biblical ideals and inspire them with determination to do so.

HOW TO USE

We suggest that each chapter be completed consecutively and used along with Companion Workbook, which brings out the Bible passages for every topic stated in the Textbook. You can split the chapters into as many days as you feel appropriate. It is not as much a matter of finishing the book quickly, as much as assimilating what is in the book .

Fathers, we urge you to participate if you can. PERSONAL HELP FOR Boys is a wonderful tool you can use to grow together with your sons in CHARACTER BUILDING.

Try just completing one chapter a week, say, together on the weekend!

We pray that you will be encouraged and enriched by this Character Study.

Yours in Christ,

PEARABLES

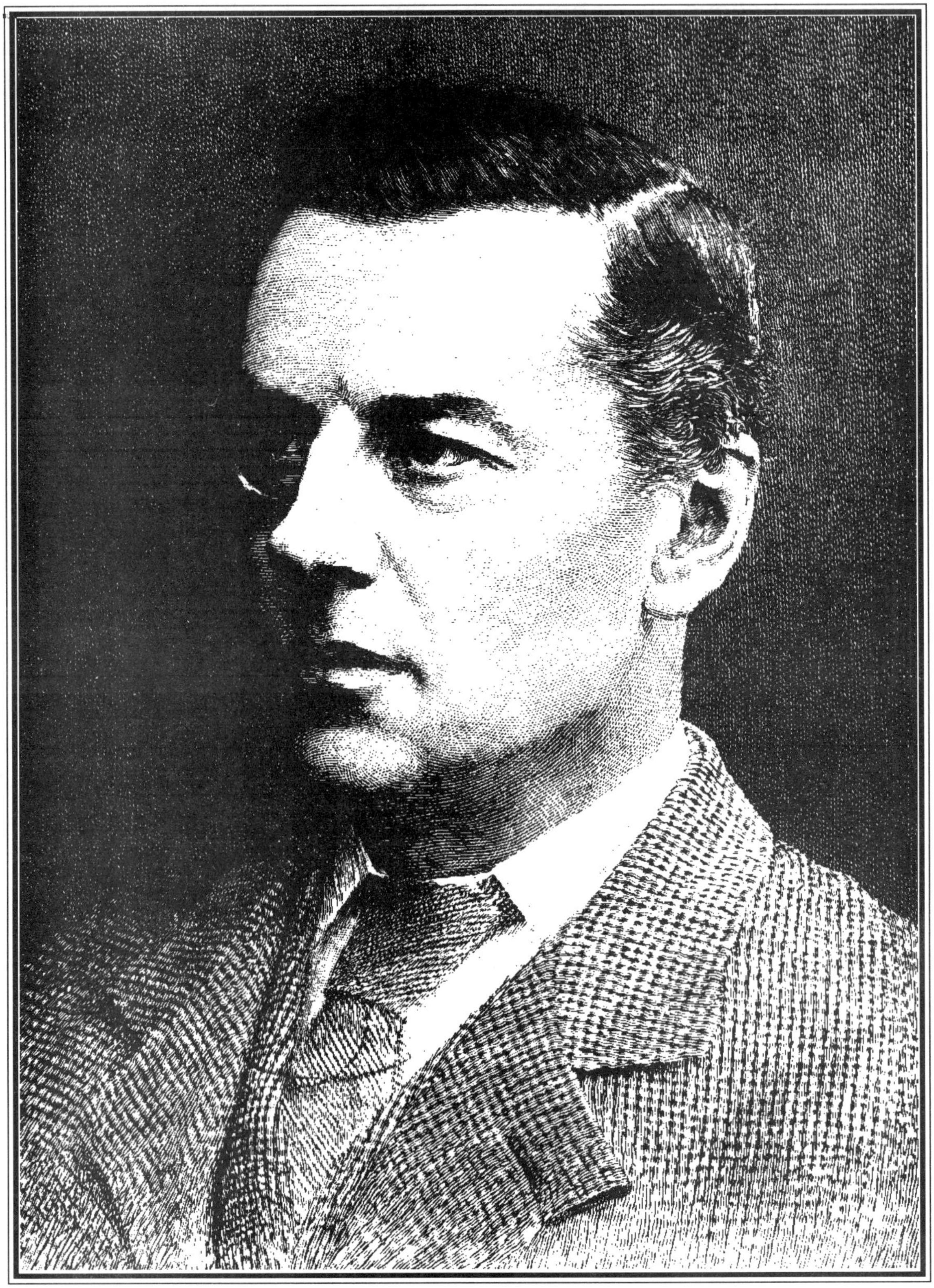

Personal Help for Boys

Chapter I

A. BOYS MAKE MEN

   1. In this chapter, what do all boys grow up to be?

   2. If a boy is not trained to work, study and know God, what will he turn out to be like when he is grown?

   3. As a boy needing to be trained, how should your attitude be?

Read: Proverbs 1:8-9

   4. What are sons to listen to?

   5. What are you not to forsake?

   6. What shall the instruction of your father and the law of your mother be to you?

📖 Chains according to this scripture mean "chains of gold about the neck", indicating political dignity. Obedience to parents is the surest way of becoming eminent among the men of God.

Read : Proverbs 3:1-4

7. What is this son not to forget here in verse 1?

8. What is his heart to keep?

9. What is the promise of verse 2, if he is obedient?

10. What two attributes in the first part of verse 3 are we not to forsake?

11. What does it mean to "bind them about thy neck"? (Compare with Prov. 1:8-9)

12. What does it mean to "write them on the tablets of your heart"? (Before you answer this question read 2 Corinthians 3:3)

13. What is the promise in verse 4, if you do these things?

Read: Proverbs 4:1-9

14. Listed in this scripture are fourteen commands and fourteen blessings. List them below:

Commands:	Blessings:
1. Hear, O Sons, Instruction of a Father	Gain Understanding
2. Give Attention	Live
3. Do not abandon my instruction	She will guard you.
4. Let your heart hold fast my words	She will watch over you
5. Keep my commandments	She will exalt you
6. Acquire Wisdom	She will honor you
7. Acquire understanding	She will place on your head a garland of grace
8. Do not forget or turn away from words of mouth	She will present you with a crown of beauty.
9. Do not forsake her	
10. Love her	
11. Prize her	
12. if you embrace her	
13.	
14.	

Read: Ecclesiastics 12:1

15. What are you to remember when you are young?

B. BOYS IMITATE MEN

1. Do you ever look at your Dad and wish to be like him in some ways?

2. It is natural that you want to be a man. You will be a man. What type of man do you desire to be?

3. How will you become this type of man?

C. A VICIOUS AND SINFUL HABIT

Read: Exodus 20:1 - 17

1. List the 10 Commandments below:

1._____
2._____
3._____
4._____
5._____
6._____
7._____
8._____
9._____
10._____

2. When you grow up, you may have to be in the presence of others who take the name of the Lord your God in vain. What will you do?

3. In verse 7 of this scripture what will God do to those who take His name in vain?

4. List the Commandment in verse 12:

5. What is the promise if you honor your parents?

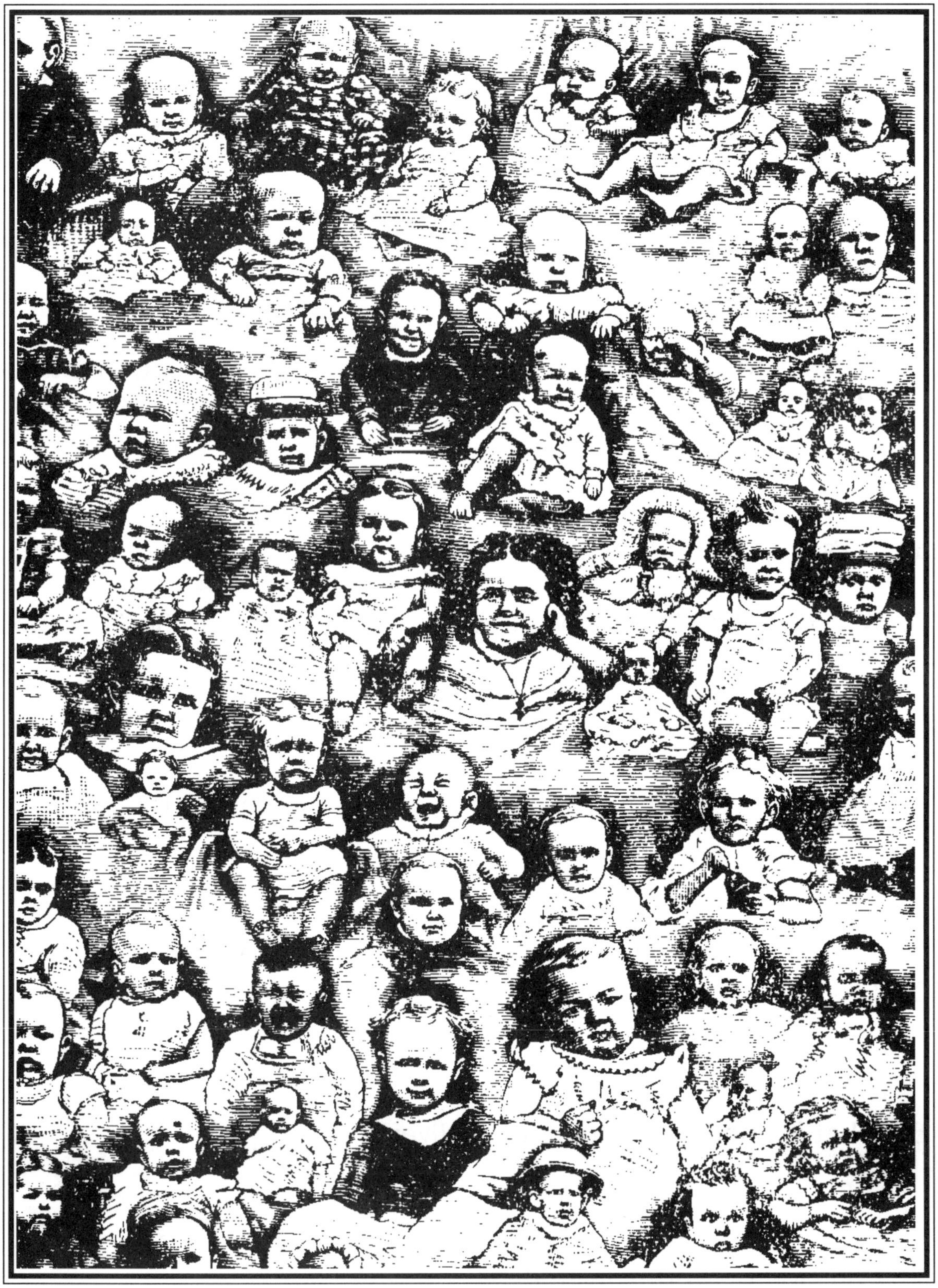

Chapter II

A. A BEAUTIFUL STORY FOR YOUNG BOYS

    1. Write in your own words a short paragraph of what this story is saying:

    2. When God created us, where were we placed for nine months while He formed us?

Read: Psalms 22:8-10

    3. Who designed that we would be taken from our mother's wombs and who took us from there?

    4. When do we start being God's, according to verse 10?

    5. A birth is sometimes called a "delivery". Did God help to "deliver" you when you were born?

    6. What is another meaning of "deliver"?

    7. Can God deliver us from evil?

Read: Isaiah 44:2

8. Who formed us?

9. If you do not like how you are formed, who are you saying did a bad job of making you?

10. Does God make mistakes?

11. Where did He create you, according to this scripture?

Read: Isaiah 49:5

12. When does God decide that one should be a servant for Him?

13. Are people created for their own purpose or for God's?

14. When we become a believer in the Messiah, Jesus, do we live for ourselves?

15. Whose good will are we to do from then on?

16. When people do not believe in God, whose will do they do?

Read :   Genesis 2:7

17. Was the first man, Adam, ever in a mother's womb.

18. How did God create him?

19. What did God breathe into the man's nostrils ?

📖 Did you know that mankind is the only creation of God to have a living soul ?

Read: Genesis 2:20 -24

20. Was the first woman ever in a mother's womb?

21. How was she created?

22. Who was the first child to be held in a mother's womb?

The True Young Knight
~Being Chilvalrous~

Chapter III

A. THE TRUE YOUNG KNIGHT

    1. According to this chapter, what are some of the attributes of a knight (Pg. 24)?

    2. How did they treat women?

    3. Are you ever unkind to your sister (if you have been blessed to have a sister)?

    4. Do you think that being unkind to anyone, even if they are bothering you, is right according to the ways of God?

B. THE SPIRIT OF CHRISTIAN CHIVALRY

    1. What is chivalry according to this book (Pg. 24-25)?

    2. Were the rules of chivalry based upon the Bible?

    Dictionary Work: CHIVALRY

    3. Write definition below:

4. What were the principles and customs of knighthood, according to this chapter?

5. Which of these attributes do you think you might wish to cultivate?

C. THE IDEAL OF TRUE MANHOOD

1. Complete the sentences below from the ideal of true manhood:

a. Fearless in the cause of _____.
b. Shrinking timidly from_____.
c. Before God humble as a _____.
d. In the presence of the wicked like a _____.
e. Docile as a _____ toward his _____.
f. Running in the race of virtue with the ardor of a _____.
g. Longing to be all in all to his _____.
h. Straining every nerve to rise to the _____.
i. Never envying the _____ of those _____.
j. Never speaking _____ of those who had _____.
k. Responding _____ and _____ to the voice _____
_____.

2. First, look up the scriptures and write them on the space given. On the blank in front of the scripture listed, write the letter from above that fits:

____2 Timothy 1:7 _____
_____
_____

____2 Corinthians 11:2_____
_____
_____

15

____1 Corinthians 11:16 _____
_____
_____
_____

____Romans 8:37 _____
_____
_____

____1 Peter 5:5 _____
_____
_____

____1 Timothy 5:1-2 _____
_____
_____

____1 Corinthians 11:3 _____
_____
_____

____2 Timothy 1:9 _____
_____
_____

____1 Corinthians 9:24 _____
_____
_____

____Ephesians 4:31 _____
_____
_____

____1 Peter 3:15 _____
_____
_____

____James 3:14 _____

_____

_____

D. FEARLESS IN THE CAUSE OF TRUTH

1. You have already looked up the scripture in 2 Timothy 1:7. What has God not given us?

2. If God has not given us the spirit of fear, what HAS he Given us?

 Dictionary Work: SOUND

3. Write the definition below:

4. Now describe below what you believe it is to have a sound mind:

5. What power do you think this is talking about?

6. We are also given LOVE. How are we to be towards our enemies?

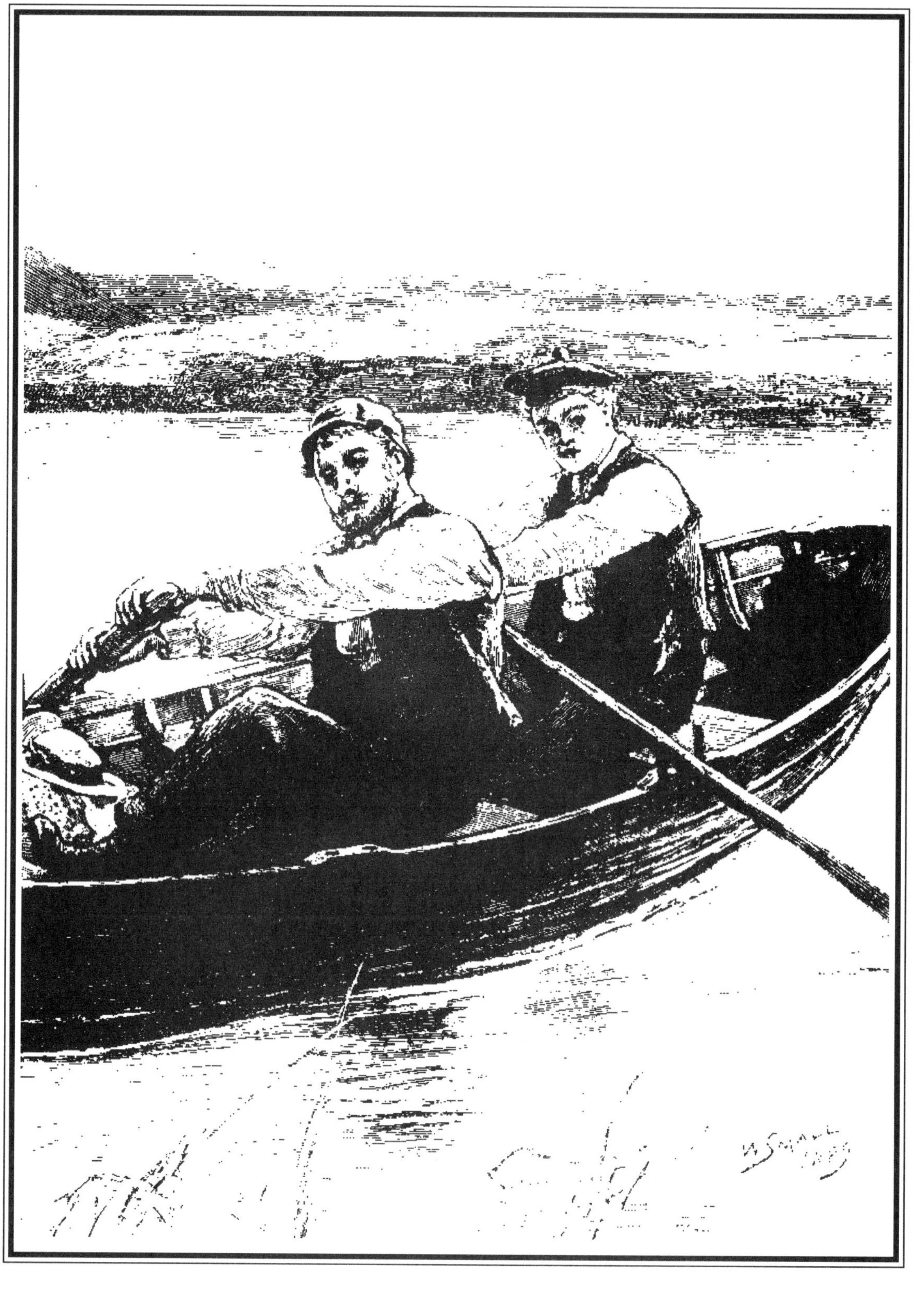

Chapter IV

A. WHAT TYPE OF MAN WILL YOU BE?

1. You have already stated what type of man you would like to become in a previous chapter. Write below what you think it is to be Godly or Holy:

Read: Psalms 24:3-5

2. Who shall ascend unto the hill of the Lord?

a. He that hath _____ hands.
b. He that hath a _____ heart.
c. Who hath not lifted up his soul unto _____.
d. Nor sworn _____.

3. Who are blessed according to this scripture?

a. Blessed are the _____.
b. Blessed are they that _____ and _____.

4. What do they do?

a. They also do _____.
b. They _____.

Read: Isaiah 35:8

5. Did you know that they had "highways" in Isaiah's time? What type of highway are they talking about here?

6. What WAY shall this be called?

Read: Matthew 5:6-8

7. Who are blessed?

8. In order to grow up to be Godly men, what must you hunger and thirst after?

9. What does it mean to be "pure in heart"?

B. A BOY SHOULD HAVE WELL-THOUGHT OUT PLANS

Read: Proverbs 3:5-6

1. Write the three commandments in this Scripture:

a. _____
b. _____
c. _____

2. What is the promise if you do these three things?

Read: Proverbs 3:7-8

3. Fill in the blanks below:

a. Be not _____ in thine own eyes.
b. F_____ the Lord and d_____ from evil.

4. Why should you do these things?

   a. It shall be_____.
   b. And_____.

5. When this chapter is telling you to have well-thought out plans, what does that consist of according to these verses?

C. DEGRADING HABITS THAT RUIN YOUR TEMPLE

   1. What were some of the vices that were mentioned in this chapter?

   2. Why do you think that the author believes these things are bad?

   3. Can you be a believer in the Lord and still do these things?

One can still be a believer and may not have yet overcome fleshly habits. When we take these things to the Lord, He will cleanse us from all ungodliness and filthiness of habit by the power of His Spirit when we yield these things to Him.

D. A BOY SHOULD PRACTICE ECONOMY

   Dictionary Work: ECONOMY

   1. Write definition below:

2. When one doesn't save a dime of any money that he chances upon, is he being economical?

3. When you are being greedy or stingy, are you being economical?

Read: Ephesians 4:19

Read: 1 Timothy 3:3 & 8

F. THE VALUE OF TIME

Read: Ephesians 5:15-16

1. What are we to redeem?

Dictionary Work: REDEEM

2. Write definition below:

3. Describe more fully what "redeeming the time" means to you:

G. THE VALUE OF UNSELFISHNESS

Read: Colossians 3:5-10

1. What are we to do with our members? _____.

2. List below the six things listed here which were to be mortified:

   1. _____
   2. _____
   3. _____
   4. _____
   5. _____
   6. _____

3. How does this relate to being selfless?

4. In verse 8, list below the six other things we are to put off:

   1. _____
   2. _____
   3. _____
   4. _____
   5. _____
   6. _____

5. What have you "put off" in verse 9? _____

6. What have you "put on" in verse 10? _____

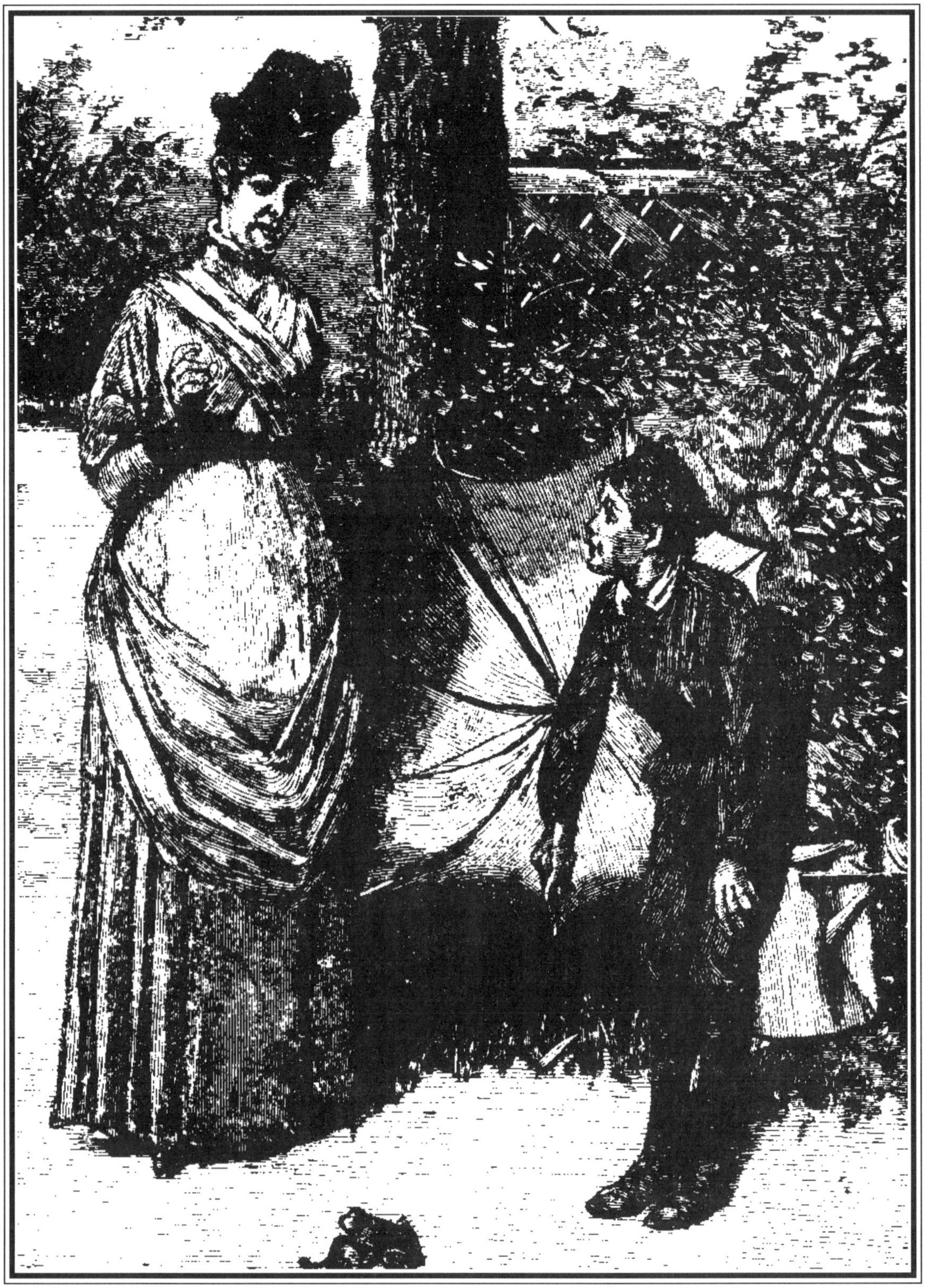

Chapter V

A. LIVING A PURE LIFE IN CHRIST

1. Sum up in your own thoughts below what this chapter is all about:

Read: Psalms 19:8

2. Fill in the correct answer below:

    a. The statutes of the Lord are _____,
_____ the heart.
    b. The _____ of the Lord is _____,
_____ the eyes.

3. Are there good things that will happen to us when we love the Word of God? What are "good things" called from God?

📖 STATUTES, according to the Strong's Concordance, regarding this scripture means: appointed, a mandate from God, a command, a law, precept, statute.

📖 COMMANDMENTS, according to this passage in the Strong's Concordance means a command, a law, ordinance, precept.

Read: Proverbs 21:8

4. Describe this scripture in your own words (you might have to look up

25

in the dictionary FROWARD):

Read: Proverbs 30:12

5. Describe what you believe is "self-righteouseness." Is it right to be "self-rightous."?

6. Can a man "save" himself?

Read: Matthew 5:8

7. What is it to have a "pure heart"?

8. Can a boy who has a "pure" heart live a "pure" life in Christ ?

📖 PURE in this scripture means "clean".

9. Have you heard the old phrase "clean living"? Describe what this means?

Read: Philippians 4:8

10. Complete the following:

    a. Whatsoever things are _____.
    b. Whatsoever things are _____.
    c. Whatsoever things are _____.
    d. Whatsoever things are _____.
    e. Whatsoever things are _____.
    f. Whatsoever things are _____.

    g. If there be any _____.
    h. If there be any_____.
    i. T_____ on these T_____.

B. WINNING THE BATTLE WITH SELF

1. The Lord has called us to "die to ourselves ". If we do this, then who are we to live in?

2. Describe below what you think of "selfishness":

Read: Proverbs 16:32

3. We are learning about "battling ourselves". What person is greater than a person who wins the battle over a city, according to this scripture?

4. Who is better than the mighty?

5. How do you control your temper?

Read: Proverbs 23:2

6. Do you think that a person that cannot control his appetite has won the battle over self?

7. Why is this wrong?

Read: John 12:25

8. What will happen to a person that loves his life?

9. What will happen to those who hate their life in this world?

    📖   Dictionary Work: HATE

10. Write definition below:

11. Describe what it means to "hate" your life in this world. Does it mean to hate yourself? Describe how it pertains to the fleshly, carnal life, not spiritual:

C. DOING GOD'S WILL, NOT SELF'S

Read: Nehemiah 9:16-17

1. Complete the sentences below:

a. But they and our fathers dealt_____.
b. And _____ their necks.
c. And _____ to Thy commandments

2. What does God think of those who are rebellious and do not do His will?

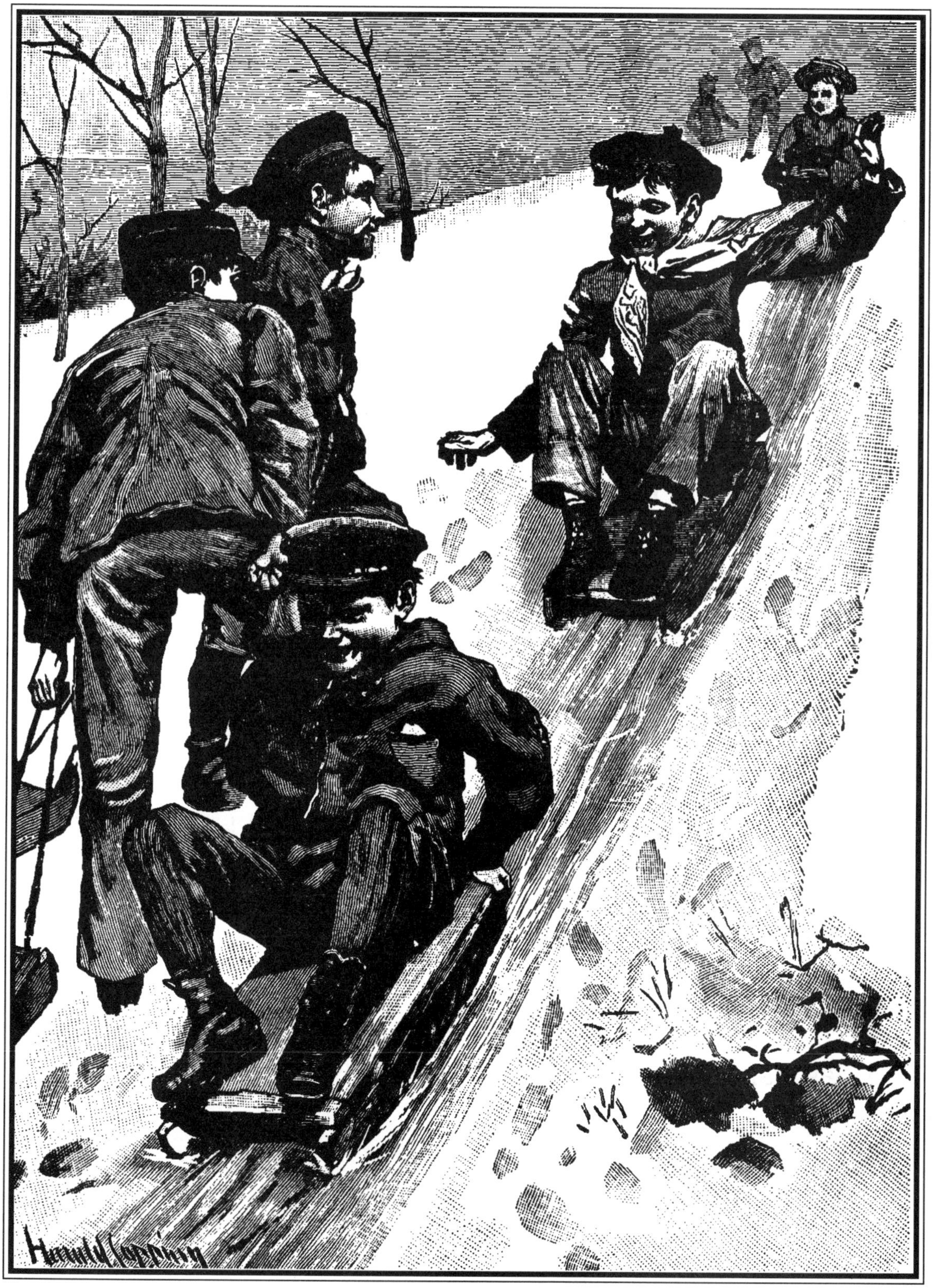

Chapter VI

A. THE WIDER MEANING OF "IDEAL BOYHOOD"

1. What is the basis for "ideal boyhood"?

2. If a person has good morals and lives a "good, clean" life, but yet they do not know Christ, are they living the ideal life?

3. What are your thoughts on "life"?

Read: Psalms 103:14

4. Complete below:

      a. For He knows our_____.
      b. He remembereth that we are _____.
      c. So... Our frame is _____.

Read: Psalms 144:4

5. According to this scripture, what two things is our life like?

Read: Ecclesiastes 6:12

6. Does a shadow come and go? Why is Solomon comparing life with a shadow?

Read: Isaiah 40:6-9

7. What is flesh likened to in this Scripture?

8. Will our physical flesh last forever?

9. What will stand forever?

Read: James 1:10

10. How are the two previous scriptures similar?

Read: James 4:14

11. How is life like a vapor?

12. Is this life ALL there is? Tell why not?

Read: Daniel 12:2

13. Many of them that sleep in the dust of the earth shall awake:
    Some to_____.
    And some to_____.

Read: Isaiah 25:8

14. In this scripture is the promise from the Lord. Write this promise below:

Read: 1 Corinthians 15:54-58

15. What has God given the Lord Jesus Christ victory over?

16. List the three things in verse 58 that you as brethren are to be:

    a. _____.
    b. _____.
    c. _____.

Read: John 17:2-3

17. What has Jesus been given?

    a. As thou hast given Him _____
    _____.

    b. That He should give _____
    _____.

18. What is life eternal?

Read: Revelation 1:18

19. What does Jesus hold the keys to?

B. A BASIS FOR THE BEST LIVING

Read: John 6:27-47

   1. Complete the following sentences:

      a. Labor not for _____.
      b. But for _____
      _____.
      c. Which the _____.

32

2. What is the work of God? (Vs. 28-29)

3. How do you live a "fulfilling" life so that you will never hunger nor thirst? (Vs. 32-35)

4. When a person believes in the Lord Jesus Christ, will they know the Father God?

C. NO BOY LIVES UNTO HIMSELF

1. "No man is a mountain" is an old adage. Please explain what this means to you:

Read: Matthew 26:39,42

2. What would have happened if Jesus would not have obeyed His Father regarding dying on the cross?

Read: Hebrews 5:8

3. Will it always be pleasant to obey the way of the gospel?

4. Whose lives does your life touch now?

5. Can you affect them for the sake of the gospel? How?

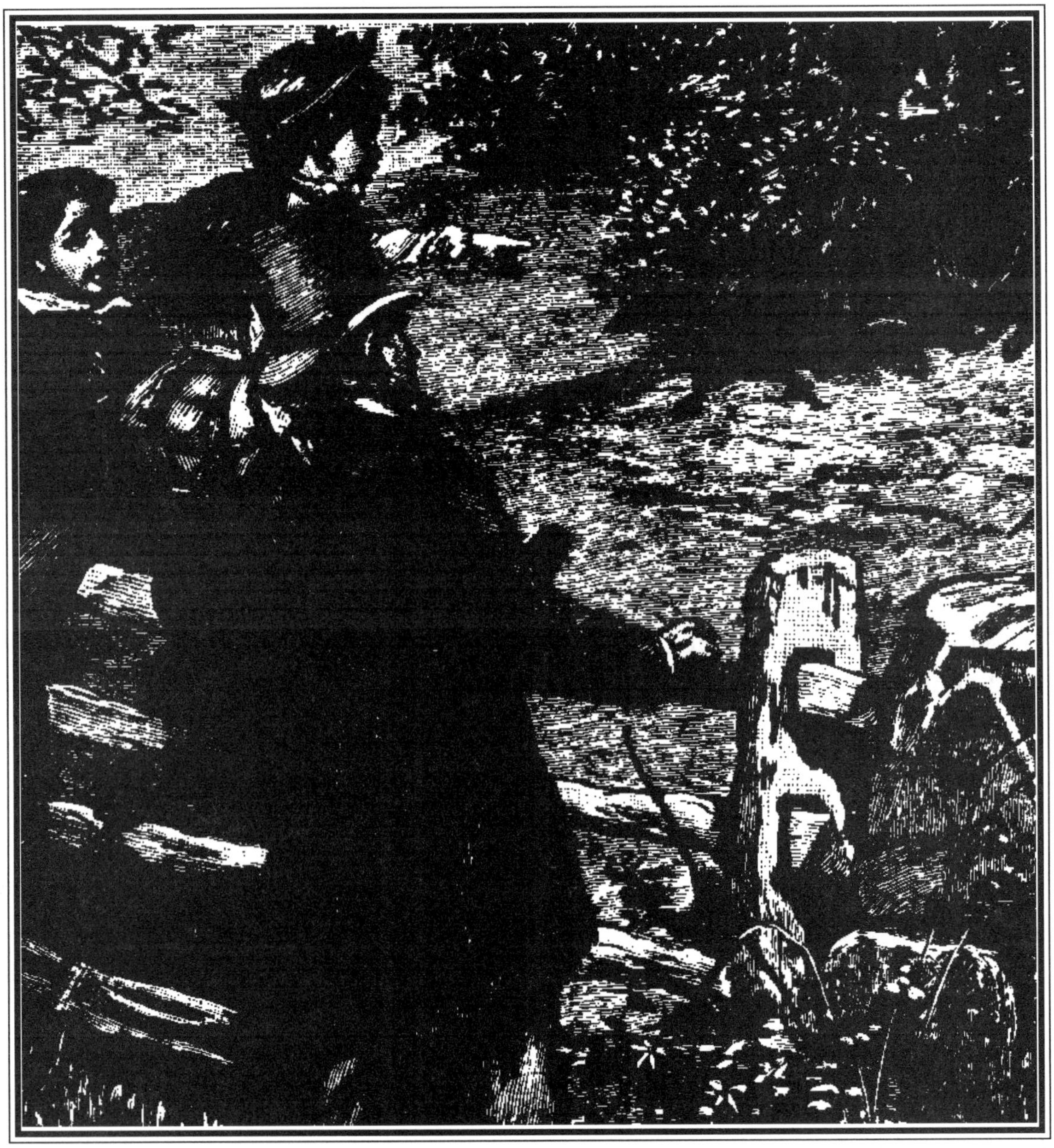

Chapter VII

A. FATHER, THE PRIEST IN THE HOME

1. What does "father, the priest in the home" mean to you?

Read: 1 Corinthians 11:3-4

2. Fill in the blanks below:

     a. But I would have you know, Brethren, that the _____ of every man is _____.
     b. That the _____ of the woman is the _____.
     c. And the _____ of Christ is _____.

3. Write the letter from above in the blank in regards to the levels of authority ordained by God:

                 First _____

                 Second _____

                 Third _____

The word HEAD here in the Strong's Concordance means from the sense of SEIZING, taken hold of, head. The dictionary defines it as being the director or chief of; to command. To assume or be placed in the first or foremost position of.

4. When you grow up, what will your position be in regards to God?

5. What will it mean to be the "head" of your family?

6. Does being the head of the family mean you only provide physical nourishment and care for your family? What other duties does the father hold in regards to Christ?

Read: 1 Peter 2:5-9

7. In verse 5, what does the scripture state believers are?

8. Who is the chief corner stone?

9. Fill in the blanks below:

   YOU ARE:
      a. A_____
      b. A_____
      c. A_____
      d. A_____

B. SPEAK RESPECTFULLY OF FATHER

   1. Is it respectful to contradict your father?

   2. God is called your Heavenly Father. Would you contradict Him?

Read: Exodus 20:12

3. What do you believe "honor" means in regards to parents?

📖   According to the Strong's Concordance, HONOR in this scripture means: numerous, be rich, honorable, glorify, and promote.

👓   Dictionary Work: HONOR

4. Write the definition below:

Read: Ephesians 6:1-2

5. Complete the sentences below:

   a. Children, _____ your parents in the Lord, for this is _____.
   b. H_____ thy father and mother; which is the first commandment with a promise.
   c. That it _____
   _____.
   And_____
   _____.

Read: Exodus 21:15-17

6. How did God feel regarding a child hitting his parents?

7. What if a person curses his father or mother?

📖   According to the Strong's CURSES here means: to make light, bring into contempt, despise, to not esteem, or to make light.

37

Read:	Proverbs 1:8

    8. What are you to hear?

Read:	Proverbs 23:22

    9. What does it mean to "hearken"?

📖 In this scripture "hearken" means: to pay attention to.

C. REMEMBERING MOTHER

    1. Who are you to honor according to the 10 commandments?

    2. How are you to treat your mother?

    3. Does talking back and arguing with your mother constitute "cursing"?

Read:	Proverbs 1:8

    4. What are you not to forsake?

    5. What do you believe "law" is here?

Read:	Proverbs 6:20

    6. Again, does mother have commands she speaks to you?

Read: Proverbs 19:26

7. Complete the following:

  a. He that _____ his father, and _____ his mother,
  b. Is a son that causes _____ and bringeth _____.

Read: Proverbs 23:22

8. What did we learn "cursing" meant? Is it a sin to "despise" one's mother?

Read: Proverbs 30:17

9. What will happen to one that mocks his father?

10. What will happen to one who despises to obey his mother?

11. Knowing what God's Word says now, how should you treat your parents?

E. TREATMENT OF BROTHER AND SISTER

1. How do you think God would have you treat you brothers and sisters?

Read: 1 John 2:9-11
    1 Corinthians 8:11-13

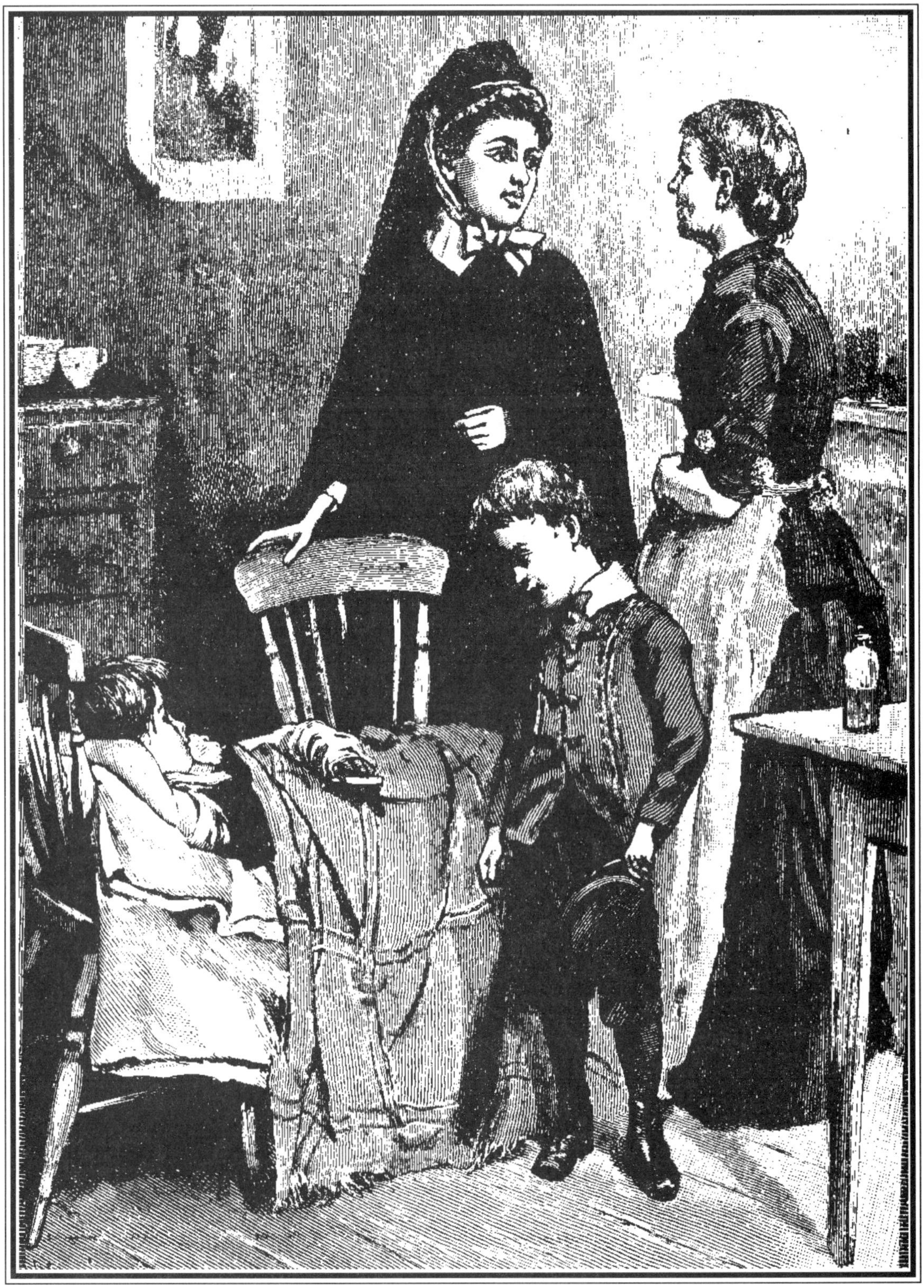

Chapter VIII

A. IDEAL BOYHOOD AND MANNERS

1. What does "good manners" mean to you?

👓   Dictionary Work: MANNERS

2. Write the definition below:

3. What do you believe is the correct way of acting towards other people?

4. Another definition was "polite bearing". Describe in your own words what this means:

👓   Dictionary Work: Etiquette

5. Write the definition below:

6. One of the definitions you found was "courteous". What do you think it means to be "courteous" to others?

Read: 1 Peter 3:8

7. We are to love other believers as brethren. If this is our example for Christian love, how ought you to treat your own brothers and sisters?

B. THE POLITE BOY

1. How do you think you are to act, if you are trying to be polite?

👓 Dictionary Work: Polite

2. Write the definition below:

3. What does being "considerate of others" mean to you?

👓 Dictionary Work: CONSIDERATE

4. How can you be considerate to those around you? List at least eight ways:

a._____
b._____
c._____
d._____
e._____
f._____
g._____
h._____

Read: Psalm 41:1

5. What are we to be considerate of in this scripture?

6. How does the world treat the poor? Do they despise them?

Read: Proverbs 29:7

7. What do the righteous consider? How can you consider the ways of the poor and help? As a child? As an adult?

C. SPEAKING TO THOSE YOU MEET

1. Why should you look people in the eye when you speak to them?

2. How can you be kind in regards to your conversation?

Read: Philippians 1:27

3. What do you think "becometh the gospel" in regards to your speech?

Read: 1 Timothy 4:12

4. Complete below:

You are to be an example of a believer in:

a._____
b._____
c._____
d._____
e._____
f._____

Read: 1 Peter 1:15

5. How are you to be, according to this scripture, regarding conversation? How an you be holy?

D. BEING WARMHEARTED, SYMPATHETIC AND KIND

1. The Bible instructs us to be kind to all, even to those who are enemies of the Christian faith. How can you be kind to your enemies even when they do bad things to you?

Read: Romans 12:10

2. How does "dying to self" relate to this scripture?

3. How are we to treat one another?

Read: 2 Corinthians 6:4-8

4. Complete the following:

But in all things approving ourselves as the ministers of God, in:

a._____
b._____
c._____

d. _____
e. _____
f. _____
g. _____
h. _____
i. _____
j. _____

By:

a. _____
b. _____
c. _____
d. _____
e. _____
f. _____
g. _____
h. _____
i. _____
j. _____
k. _____

As:

a. _____
b. _____
c. _____
d. _____
e. _____
f. _____
g. _____

Read: Colossians 3:12
2 Peter 1:7

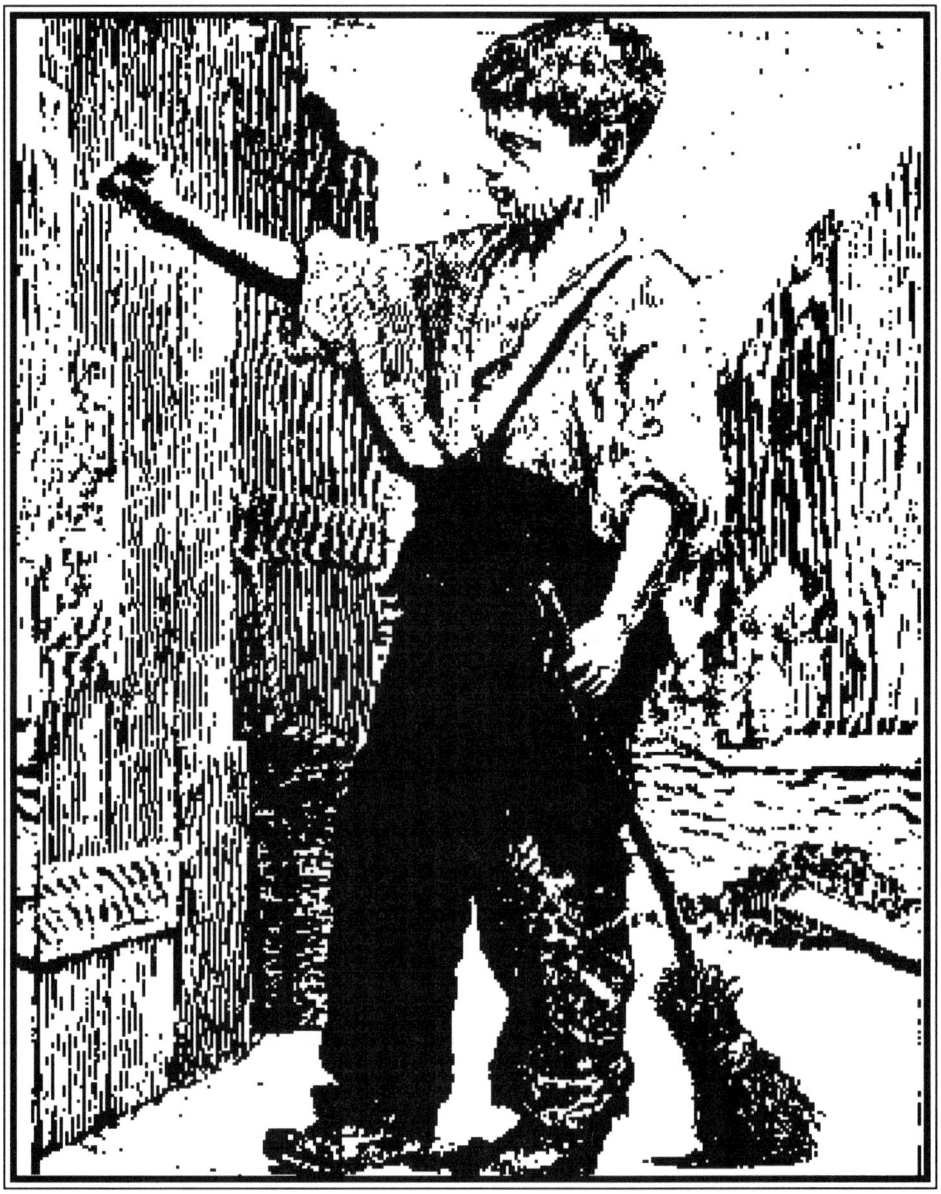

Chapter IX

A. IDEAL BOYHOOD IN WRITING

    1. What is this chapter all about?

    2. Do you believe that you are diligent when you write?

    3. In the beginning, was the Word of God written by a typewriter or a computer?

    4. How was the Bible written?

    5. If the people who wrote the Bible had to write by hand, do you think they had to be careful so people could read it?

    6. When you write, why is it a courtesy to write nicely and to make your letters readable?

Read: Isaiah 1:17

    7. The first part of this scripture is TO LEARN TO DO WELL. How can we say that writing carefully compared to slothfully is learning to do well?

    8. We want to write legibly. What do you think legibly means?

👓　　　Dictionary Work:　　　LEGIBLY

9. Write the definition below:

10. Can you think of any reason a sensible boy would wish to write any other way than legible?

Read:　　Philippians 2:14

11. When you mother or father requests that you practice your handwriting and to write legibly, how are you to respond?

Read:　　Colossians 3:17

12. How are you to do all things? Would you write a sloppy, unreadable letter to the Lord?

B. POOR SPELLING

1. Why is it important to know how to spell?

2. When you grow up you will need to know how to spell when you have your profession. List five reasons why it is important to have good spelling:

a._____
b._____
c._____
d._____
e._____

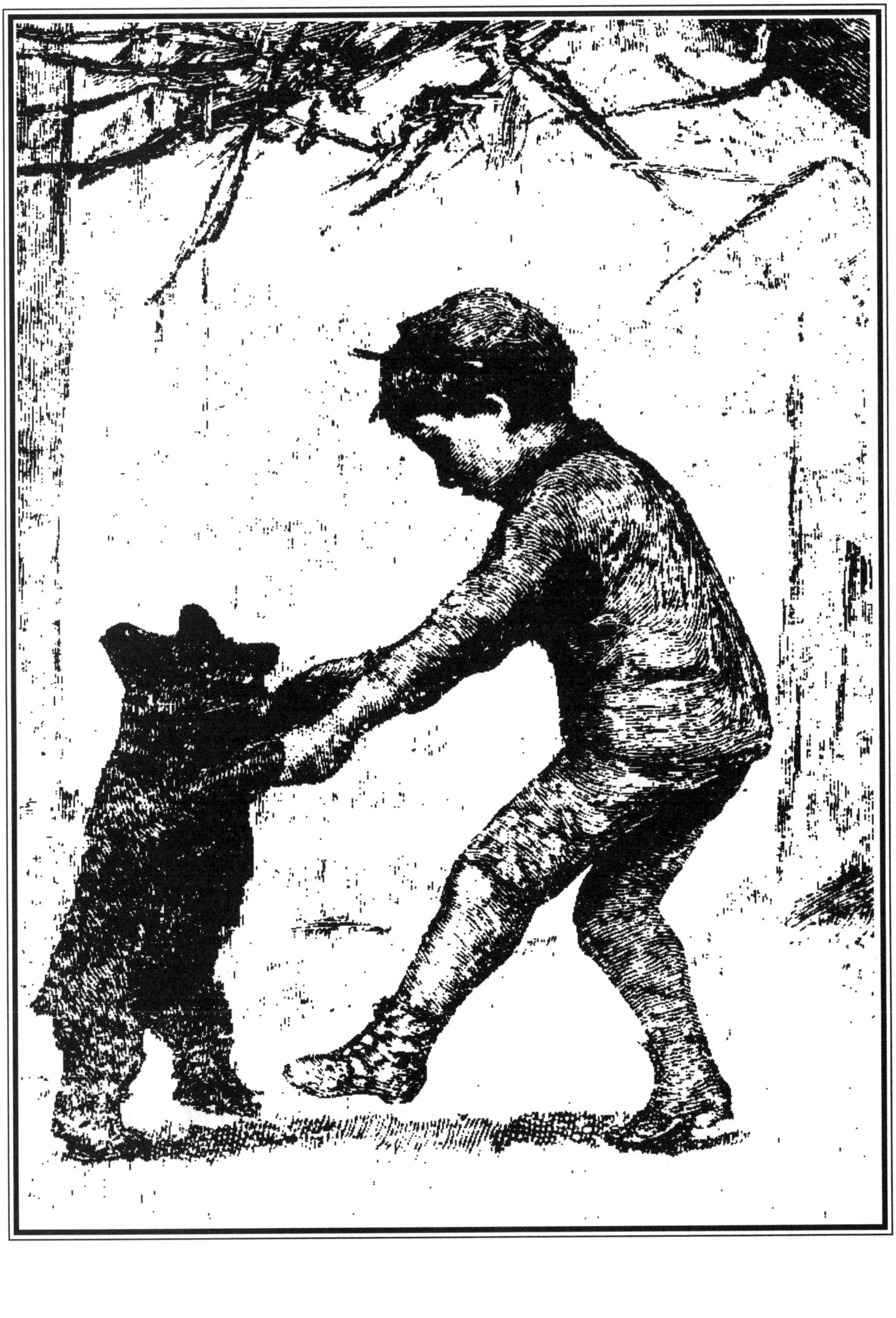

Chapter X

A. IDEAL BOYHOOD IN READING

1. Why is it important that every boy learn to read?

2. What is the first book that you should cultivate reading?

3. The Bible contains all knowledge of life and gives us instruction. Why do people read other books than the Bible?

a._____

b._____

c._____

d._____

Read: 2 Timothy 2:15

4. According to this Scripture, why are you to study?

5. What does "approved" mean?

📖   According to the Strong's Concordance APPROVED means to be accounted; accepted; tried.

6. What are you to study?

B. A BOY'S TASTE IN READING

   1. What type of reading material do you think God would have you read?

   2. What do you think God thinks of "fiction"?

Read: 2 Corinthians 10:5

   3. What are we to cast down?

   4. How does this pertain to reading things that do not have anything to do with God?

   5. What are VAIN imaginations? (Read Romans 1:21)

C. LEARNING THE MEANING OF NEW WORDS

   1. In the Bible there are many new words which we can learn from. List below some suggestions that this chapter gave in regards to new, unfamiliar words:

   _____
   _____
   _____
   _____
   _____
   _____
   _____

51

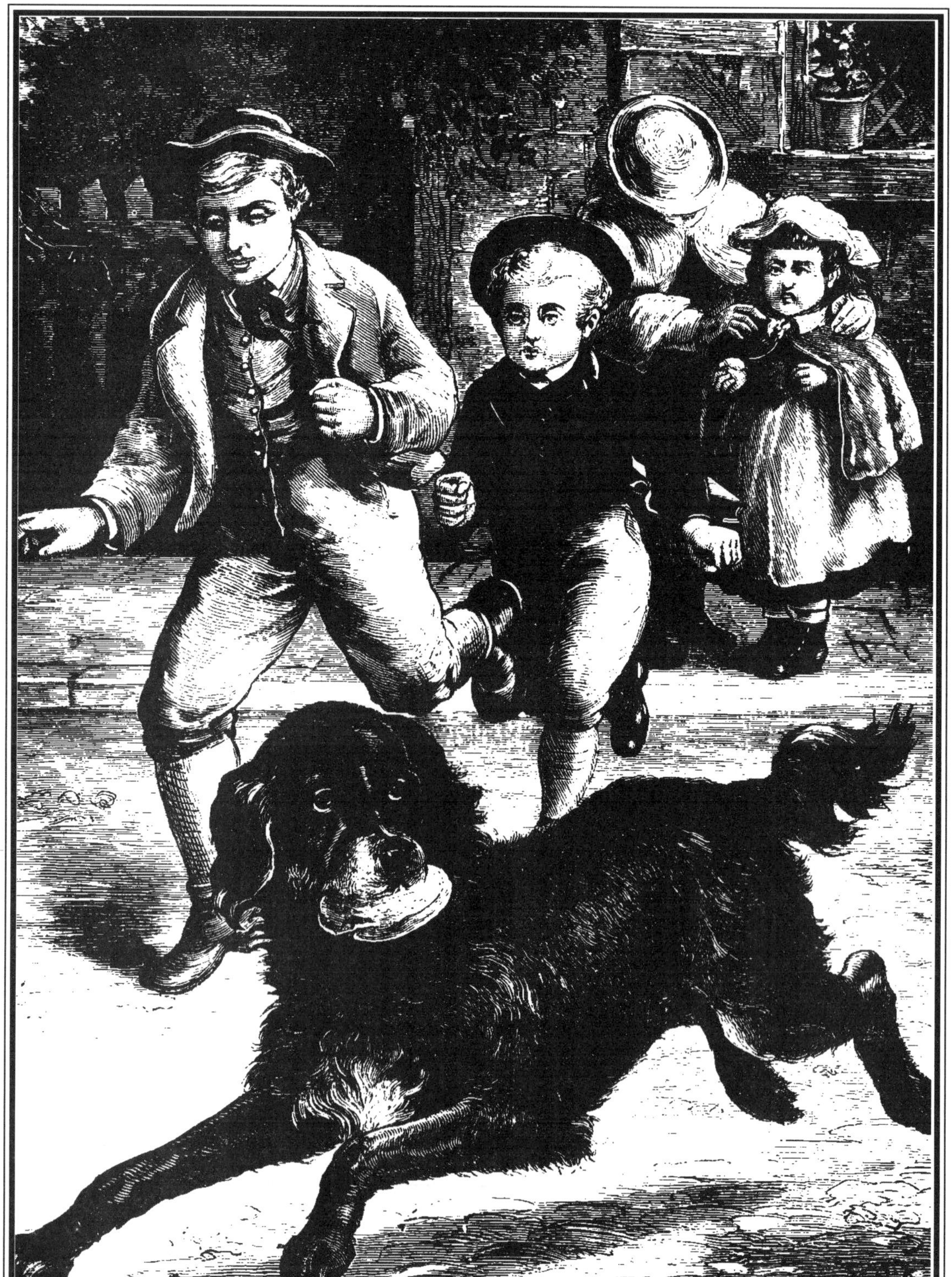

Chapter XI

A. SOME GOOD "GUIDEPOSTS" TO IDEAL BOYHOOD

1. What is a "guide post"?

Dictionary Work: GUIDE POST

2. Write definition below:

Some very old guide posts were nothing but a mound of stone with an arrow and a coarsely chiseled stone marker on the top. But these guide posts were very important as they pointed the correct way towards food and shelter. So are the following guide posts, especially the sixth. The sixth guide post tells us to only go with the Word of God and what it tells us rather than by our feelings. Our feelings are deceitful, but the Word of God is truth!

B. STUDY DETAILS

1. Would you consider yourself someone who is a "watcher"? That means someone who looks around him rather than concentrating only on self?

Read: 1 Corinthians 16:13-14

2. List the five commands in this scripture:

a._____
b._____
c._____

        d._____
        e._____

    3. What do you believe we are to "watch" for?

Read: 1 Thessalonians 5:6

    4. What does it mean to "watch and be sober"?

Read: 2 Timothy 4:5

    5. Are we to "watch" just part of the time?

Read: 1 Peter 4:7

    6. What are we to "watch" unto here?

    7. Why is PRAYER important?

C. PROFIT BY EXPERIENCE

    1. When someone "profits" from something, what does this mean?

    ⌐⌐ Dictionary Work: PROFIT

    2. Write the definition below:

54

3. How can you profit from other people's mistakes?

4. Have you ever learned something from a mistake? Tell a story below about what you have learned and how:

D. STICK CLOSER TO THE HARD TASKS

1. What does DILIGENCE mean to you? What does it mean to do something diligently?

2. Does it take a man to be diligent? Can a boy be diligent?

    Dictionary Work: DILIGENCE

3. Write the definition below:

Read: Proverbs 4:23

4. What are you to keep with all diligence?

5. What does that mean to you?

Read: 2 Corinthians 8:7

6. List the seven things you are to abound in:

a. _____
b. _____
c. _____
d. _____
e. _____
f. _____
g. _____

E. OBEY ORDERS

1. According to the Bible, who are those you are to obey?

Read: Deuteronomy 21:18-20

2. Who is a child to obey in this scripture? What was the terrible punishment if he did not obey?

Read: Acts 5:29

3. Who are we to obey? What is a person called who wants to only obey men? Who will you obey?

Read: Colossians 3:22

4. This scripture is for those who serve others. How should you treat your employers?

Read: Hebrews 13:17

5. List below some people who have the rule over you now, and those who will also in the future?

a._____
b._____
c._____
d._____
e._____
f._____

Read: 1 Peter 1:22

6. How are we to obey? Who will help us?

F. LOOK AT BOTH SIDES

1. In everything, there are usually two sides to every story. When you grow up you may become a boss. Why is it important that you learn to listen to both sides? Why is it important to put ourselves in someone else's shoes?

2. How are believers to judge? Are we to show partiality?

Read: 1 Corinthians 5:12-13

3. What is this scripture talking about?

4. Who are we to judge?

📖   In the Strong's Concordance, JUDGE here means distinguish, decide; to try; punish; decree...

Read: 1 Corinthians 6:2-5

5. If the saints are to judge the world, why is it important to look at both sides of an issue?

6. BUT, are there two sides to an issue regarding sin?

7. What is SIN?

8. If you know someone is in sin because they have disobeyed the Word of God rebelliously, is there another side? Is there an excuse?

G. LIVE BY REASON ACCORDING TO GOD'S WORD, NOT BY FEELINGS

1. Do you believe that we can count more on our feelings rather than God's Holy Word?

2. Why is it important to live by God's Word?

Read: Proverbs 22:15

3. What is bound in the heart of a child?

Read: Proverbs 28:26

4. Should a man trust in his own heart?

5. What is a man that trusts in his own heart?

Read: Ephesians 4:17-19

6. What is "the vanity of their mind"? Could that be their feelings and thoughts?

7. Are we to walk this way?

H. "SAFETY FIRST"

1. In this day and age we find many men who grow up to be "thrill seekers". What is a "thrill seeker"?

2. What do you think God thinks of those who only live from pleasure to pleasure?

3. Do they worry about maybe getting hurt?

4. When you are an employee, or even an employer, you must be cautious for the safety of others and yourself. How might you be cautious?

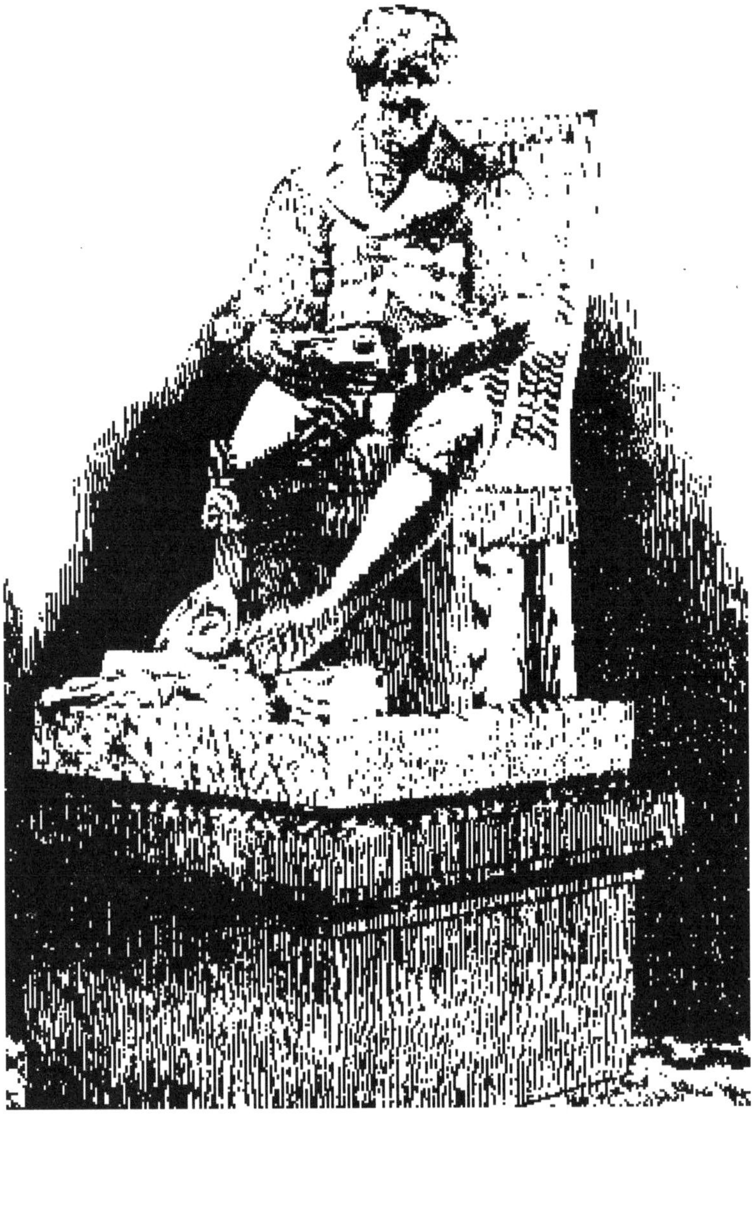

Chapter XII

A. THE NEED FOR CHRIST IN OUR LIVES

1. How important is it that we have Christ in our lives?

2. How important is it that we LIVE in Christ?

3. How does one live in Christ?

Read: John 1:7-12

4. Complete the following sentences:

    a. The same came for a _____, to bear witness of the _____, that _____ men through Him might _____.
    b. He was not that _____, but was sent to bear witness of that _____.
    c. _____ was the true _____, which lighteth every _____ that cometh into the world.
    e. He came unto His _____, and his _____ received Him not.
    f. But as _____ as _____ Him, to them gave He _____ to become the sons of _____, even to them that _____ on His Name.

5. How does one become a son of God?

6. Whose name must one believe?

Read: Acts 13:39

7. By WHOM are we justified from all things?

8. Could one be justified by the Law of Moses?

Read: Acts 16:31

9. What must one do to be saved?

10. Saved from what?

11. What is eternal death?

B. THE NEED FOR GODLY FELLOWSHIP

1. What does "fellowship" mean to you?

 Dictionary Work: FELLOWSHIP

2. Write the definition below:

3. What type of fellowship should you try to cultivate in your life?

4. Are there types of fellowship you should avoid?

Read: 2 Corinthians 6:14

   5. Complete the following:

      a. Be not _____

_____

     Why? b. For what _____

_____?

      c. And what _____

_____?

6. Explain why you should not be unequally yoked together with unbelievers, in your own words.

   7. Give an example of what "being unequally yoked" might mean:

Read: Ephesians 5:11

   8. What are you not to have fellowship with?

Read: 1 John 1:3-7

   9. With WHOM are you to have fellowship with?

   10. How will you know one another?

C. RELATIONSHIP WITH GOD

1. Relationship with God is even more important than having a relationship with other people. If you have many people in your life, but you neglect to really KNOW God, is that having a relationship with God?

2. How can you have RELATIONSHIP with God?

Read: 1 Corinthians 1:9

3. With WHOM are we called into fellowship in this verse?

4. Who called us?

Read: Deuteronomy 10:12

5. What does God require of you?

Read: Mark 12:29-33

6. What is the first of all the commandments?

One can know OF God but never get to KNOW Him. But, the Lord promises "If we seek Him, we will find Him!"

D. TALK TO GOD IN PRAYER

1. What is prayer?

👓   Dictionary Work: PRAYER

2. Write the definition below:

Read: Colossians 1:9

3. What did the believers in this scripture not cease in?

Read: 1 Thessalonians 5:17

4. What are WE not to cease in?

Read: James 5:13-16

5. What are you to do if you are afflicted? What will save him?

E. NEVER BE ASHAMED TO CONFESS JESUS

1. In the world in which we live, many people make fun of Jesus or those who believe in Him. In the work force, you may find yourself in some situations where others might pressure you into ungodly requests. What will you do?

2. Should you ever be ashamed to confess that you believe in the Lord Jesus Christ?

Read: Mark 8:38

   3. Is it a terrifying thing to be ashamed of Jesus?

Read: Romans 1:16

   4. Were the apostles ashamed of the gospel of Christ? Why not?

Read: 2 Timothy 2:15

   5. What will help a person not to be ashamed, according to this verse?

Read: 1 Peter 4:16

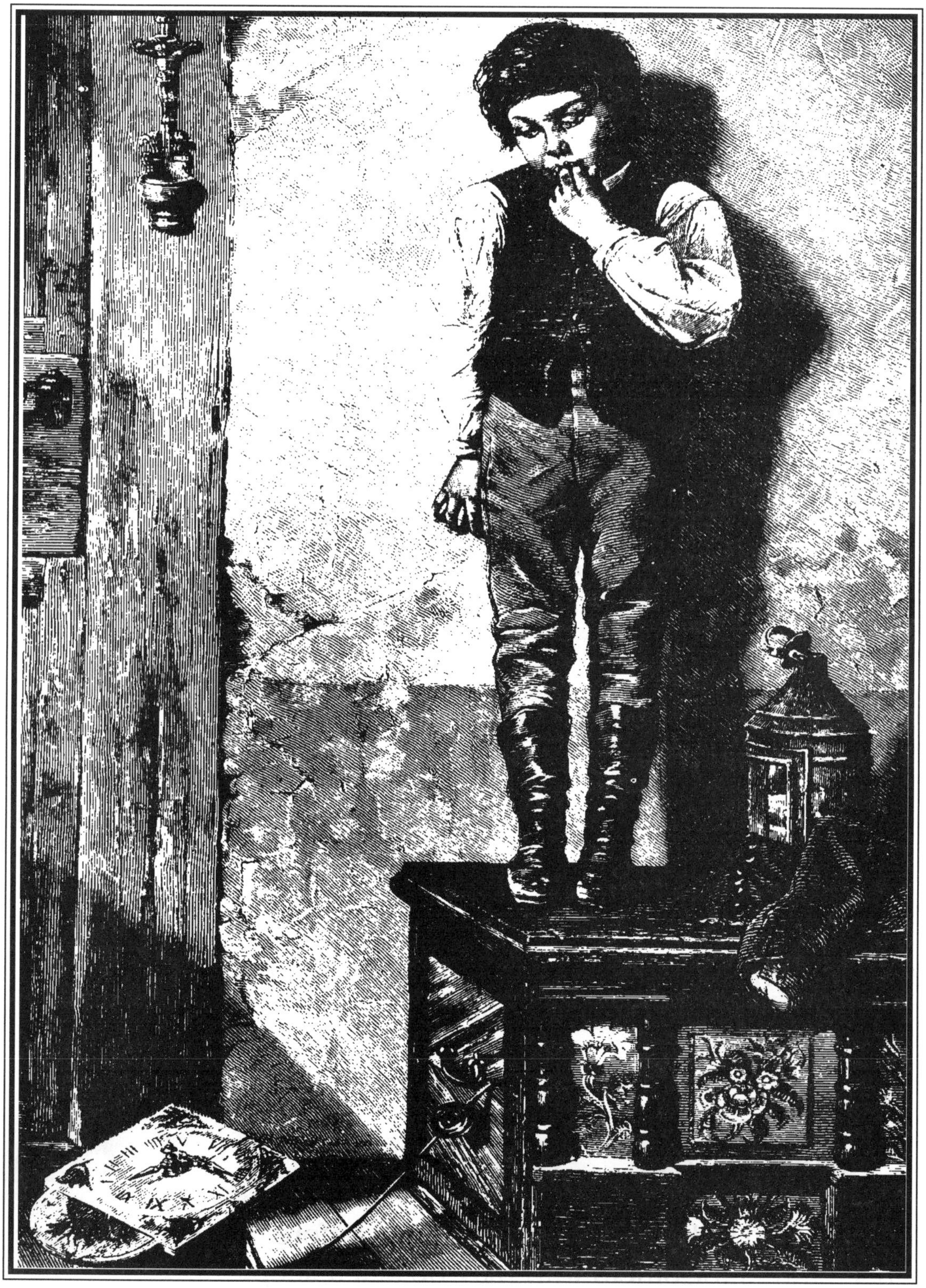

Chapter XIII

A. A FEW BYLAWS FOR DAILY LIVING

   1. What is a BYLAW?

   Dictionary Work: BYLAW

   2. Write the definition below:

These are rules that you decide to live by. The following BYLAWS are all based upon principles in the Bible!

B. BE AN EARLY RISER

   1. Why is it good to be an early riser? What do you think God thinks of those who sleep until noon?

Read: Psalms 5:3

   2. "In the morning" means early in the morning. What are we to first do in the morning, according to this scripture?

Read: Proverbs 27:14

   3. When you wake in the morning early before others are up, are you to have consideration for others who may be still asleep?

C. RETIRE AT A CERTAIN HOUR

1. Many people in the world stay up all hours of the night in drunken revelries and parties. Is this good? What will it do to your body, the temple of the Lord?

Read: 1 Thessalonians 5:4-5

2. Complete the following:

a. But you brethren are not _____

b. That day should _____

c. Ye ARE all the _____

d. We are NOT _____

D. BE AN "ON TIMER"

1. What does it mean to be "ON TIME"?

2. When a person does not keep their word and be at a certain place when they have agreed to be, does this show that they are considerate of others? Explain:

Read: Psalms 119:60

3. What are we never to DELAY or BE LATE in?

69

E. KEEP YOUR WORD

    1. If a person says something but then does not do it, are they lying?

    2. When you tell someone you will do something, ought you to do it?

Read: James 5:12

    3. Explain this scripture:

F. CONTROL YOUR TEMPER

    1. Do you ever get angry? What makes you angry? Is it biblical to get angry?

    2. If you are angry, will you have many friends?

Read: Ephesians 4:31

    3. Complete the following:

    PUT AWAY FROM YOU:

        a._____
        b._____
        b._____
        d._____
        e._____
        f._____

Read: Titus 1:7

    4. What must a bishop be? Is he quick-tempered?

G. LEARN TO BE PATIENT

    1. Patience is a wonderful virtue. What does being "patient" mean to you?

Read: Ecclesiastics 7:8

    2. Is it good to be patient in spirit? Why?

Read: 1 Thessalonians 5:14

    3. How are you to be towards ALL men?

Read: James 5:7-8

    4. Complete the following:

       a. Be _____ therefore, brethren, unto the coming of the Lord.
       b. Behold the husbandman _____ - for the precious fruit of the earth, and hath long _____ for it, until he receive the early and latter rain.
       c. By ye also _____; establish you hearts; for the coming of the Lord draweth nigh.

H. NEVER BE RESENTFUL

1. What does it mean to RESENT someone? Have you ever resented anyone? Do you think that this is pleasing to God? How must you stop resenting others?

📖   Another word for RESENTFUL is BITTERNESS. They mean the same thing.

Read: Ephesians 4:31

2. What does bitterness breed?

Read: Hebrews 12:15

3. What defiles in this scripture?

I. ADMIT IT IF WRONG

1. The most courageous thing a man can do is to admit when he is wrong. Why does it take courage?

📖   Another word for ADMITTING YOUR WRONGS is REPENTANCE or CONFESSING YOUR SINS.

Read: James 5:16

2. What are we to confess to one another?

3. What will happen if you confess them, according to this scripture?

Read: 1 John 1:9

4. What happens in this scripture when we confess our sins?

J. BE CANDID

1. What does it mean to be CANDID?

Another word for CANDID is HONESTY.

Read: Romans 13:13

2. How are we to walk? What do you think "walk" means?

Read: 2 Corinthians 13:7

3. What are you to do in this scripture?

K. BE GENEROUS

1. Describe what a person is like when they have a generous spirit:

Read: Romans 12:8

2. In this scripture, how is one to give?

Read: Acts 2:42-47

3. Describe how you may live this scripture out today:

L. BE ACCOMMODATING

1. Would you say that you are accommodating? Explain how:

Another word for ACCOMMODATING is ACCORD. To bring into accord.

Dictionary Work: ACCORD

2. Write the definition below:

Read: Acts 4:24

3. What did the believers do in one accord here?

Read: Philippians 2:2

4. Explain in this scripture what being of one accord means:

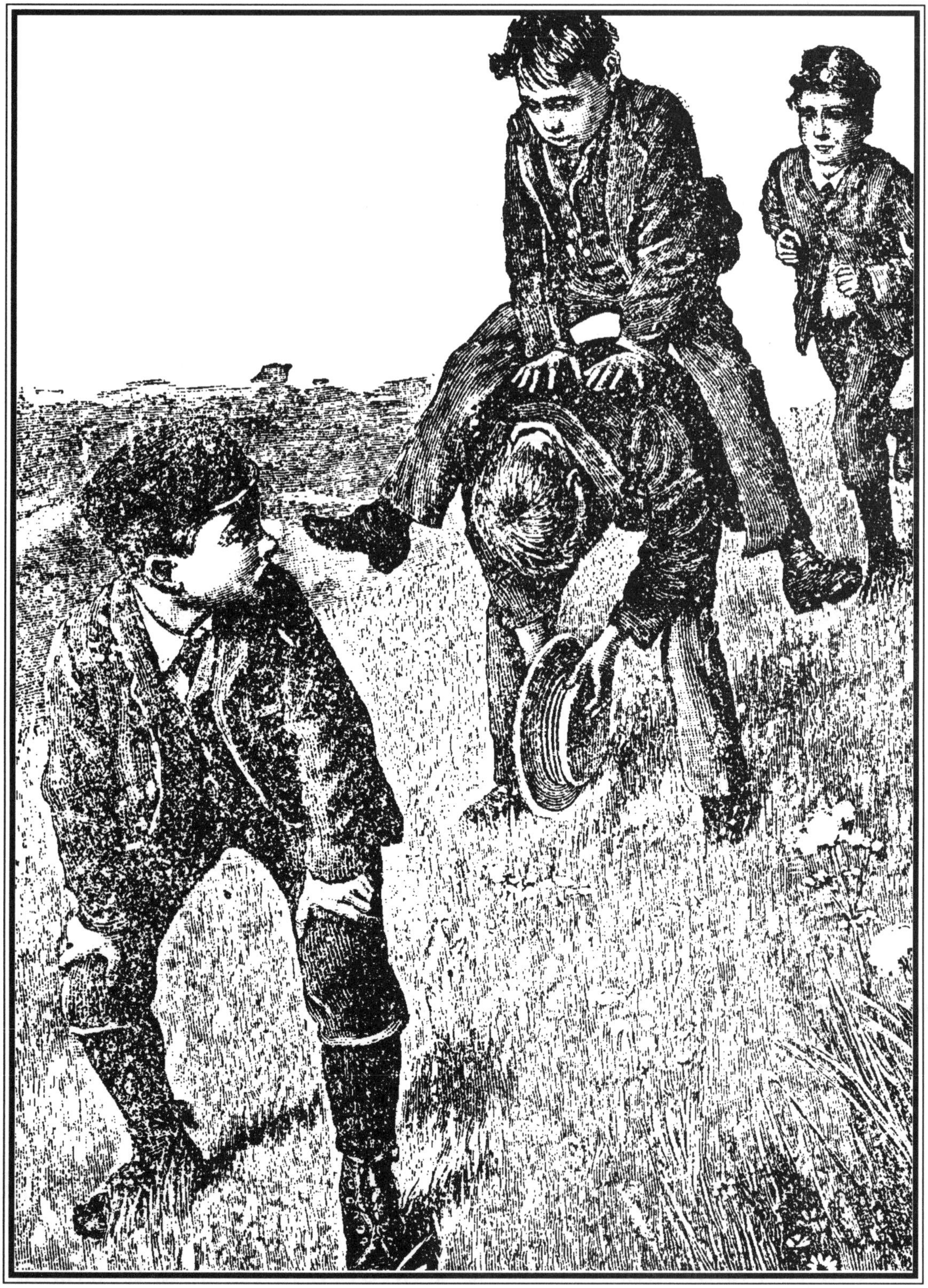

Chapter XIV

A. ASSOCIATIONS

1. Describe what "associations" are:

2. Make a list of the friends you have:

_____
_____
_____
_____
_____
_____

3. Did you know that the Bible tells us to be very careful with whom we associate? What does "associate" mean to you?

> Dictionary Work: ASSOCIATE

4. Write the definition below:

5. In some context of the definition it means to UNITE. The Bible tells us that we must only unite or yoke ourselves together with believers. Why do you think it says this?

B. YOUR CHOICE OF FRIENDS

1. Did you know that you make a CHOICE in regards to friends? What type of people do you choose to befriend?

Read: 2. Corinthians 6:14

2. Complete the following:

a. BE YE NOT _____

_____

b. For what _____

_____

c. And what _____

_____

3. What would you have in common with someone who does not love the Lord?

4. What would you have to talk about with people like that?

5. Does this mean that you do not witness or tell others about the Lord?

C. BAD COMPANY

1. The Bible warns us all throughout its pages to watch out for bad company. What do you think is "bad company"?

Read: Exodus 23:2

2. If the people of the land ALL go their own way and do things that are contrary to the Bible, are you to follow? What will you do?

Read: Proverbs 26:4-5

3. What do you think "SIT" means in this verse?

📖 According to the Strong's Concordance, SIT here means to dwell, to remain, to settle, to marry!

Read: Psalms 101:4

4. What do you think it means to "KNOW" a wicked person? We all know OF wicked people, so what is this telling you?

Read: Proverbs 1:10-15

5. What are you to do if someone tries to get you to do evil?

Read: Proverbs 4:14-15

6. When you know someone is not following the Lord, are you to befriend them? How do you tell them about God? Is there a difference between befriending someone and witnessing to someone that is willing to hear?

📖 In God's Word the apostles all witnessed to people. They preached the gospel and those that listened followed and they had fellowship with them because they believed. The ones who didn't want the gospel did not want to remain with them and they departed. You must never pretend to be part of the world, for you are not. You do not try to fit in with the ways of the world, only stand for the ways of the Word!

Read: Proverbs 14:7

7. When are you to leave the presence of a foolish person (one who is devoid of the love of God)?

Read: Jeremiah 15:17

8. Is it better to be with others who are going the WRONG way, or to be alone and go the RIGHT?

D. A MAN IS KNOWN BY HIS FRIENDS

1. Did you know the Bible tells us that we will become like those with whom we associate? Why do you think this is so?

Read: Proverbs 13:20

2. With whom should you walk? What type of "wisdom" are they talking about here?

Read: Proverbs 22:24-25

3. Why are you not to make friends with an angry man?

Read: Proverbs 16:29

4. Is a violent man and an angry man very similar? Explain:

Read: 1 Corinthians 15:33

5. According to this scripture, will GOOD company make the bad good?

6. What happens?

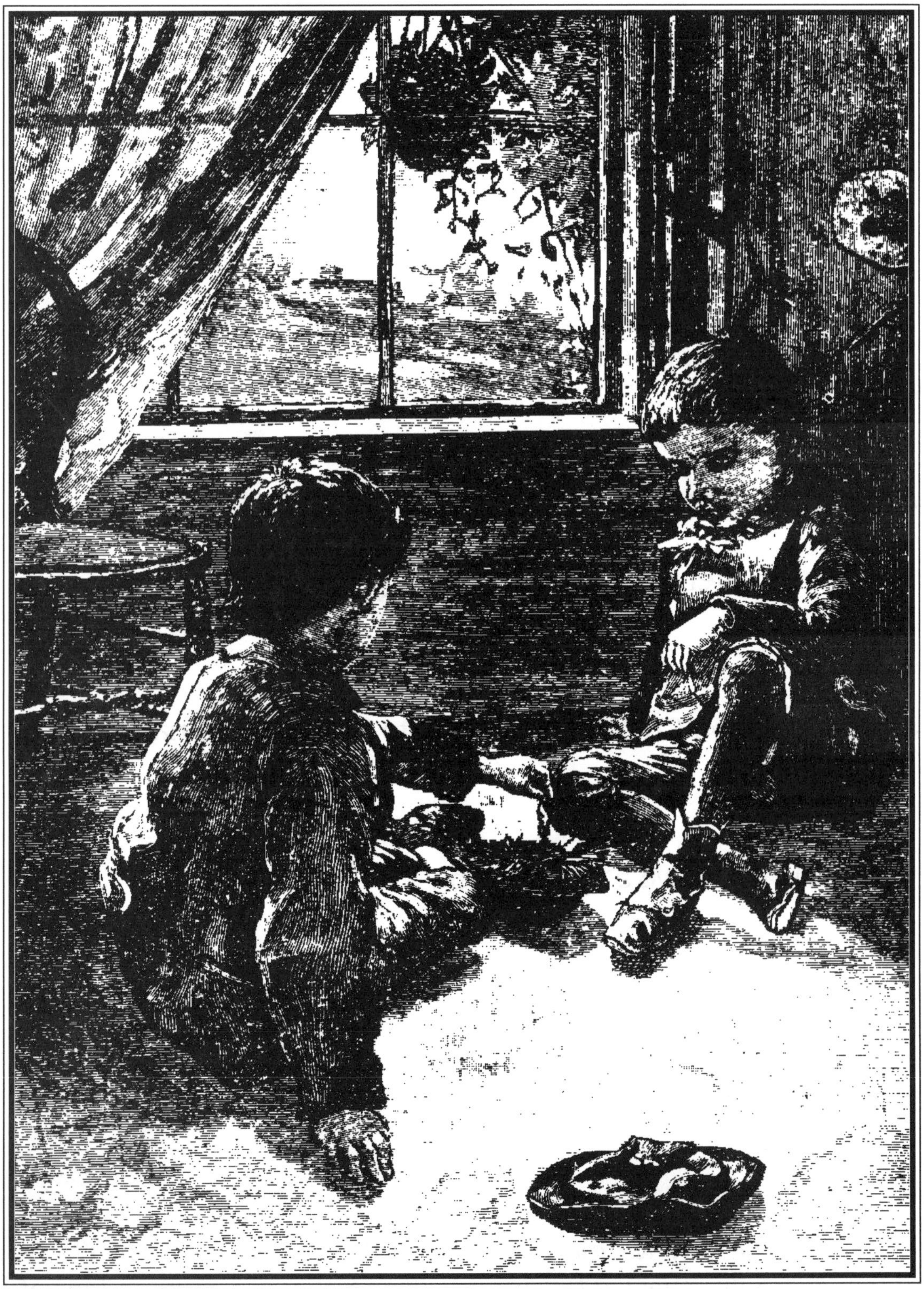

Chapter XV

A. CHARACTER

   1. What do you believe is Godly "character"?

   Dictionary Work: CHARACTER

   2. Write the definition below:

Read: Proverbs 22:1

   3. What is better to be CHOSEN than great riches?

   4. Can a person CHOOSE or decide to have a good name?

   5. What is it to have a "good name"?

Read: Ecclesiastics 7:1

   6. What is better than precious ointment?

   7. Why is the day we die better than the day we are born? Does our society view death like this? Why should we as believers have no fear of death?

According to the Thesaurus, character means moral and ethical strength.

8. What does it mean to be ethical?

Dictionary Work: ETHICAL

9. Write the definition below:

B. THE IMPORTANCE OF EXAMPLES

1. Can you list below some examples of why the men below had Godly character?

Daniel_____

_____
_____
_____

Noah_____

_____
_____
_____

David_____

_____
_____
_____

Paul_____

_____
_____
_____

2. Read the scripture then write on the line what character attribute is listed.

   a. John 10:3-4 _____
   b. Philippians 2:15 _____
   c. Proverbs 28:1 _____
   d. Acts 8:2 _____
   e. Revelation 17:14 _____
   f. John 1 _____
   g. Psalms 34:2 _____
   h. Romans 16:19 _____
   i. Matthew 5:8 _____
   j. Acts 2:42 _____

C. FORMATION OF GODLY CHARACTER

1. When we say that we want to have a Godly character, that means that we want to have a countenance that reflects God. We wish to hold the morals and ethics that are taught in His Word. How can we help to acquire a Godly Character?

2. Can you do it all by YOURSELF? Who must help you?

3. What does having a Godly Character have to do with being "born again"?

D. BEING UPRIGHT AND VIRTUOUS

1. What do "upright" and "virtuous" mean?

☙ Dictionary Work: UPRIGHT

2. Write the definition below:

☙ Dictionary Work: VIRTUE

3. Write the definition below:

Read: Psalms 94:15

4. What shall the upright in heart follow? What are God's judgments?

Read: Psalms 112:2

5. What will happen to the upright in this scripture?

Read: Proverbs 11:20

6. What are the upright in this scripture?

Read: Proverbs 15:8

7. What is God's delight?

Read: Philippians 4:8

8. List all the things we are to think on:

9. How do television and some fiction novels compare with this scripture? Do they line up with this passage?

Read: 2 Peter 1:3-5

10. What are we to add? What does virtue come after? What comes after virtue?

E. TRUE CHARACTER COMES FROM GOD

1. The more we love God, the more we will have a Godly character. Explain:

Read: Psalms 57:7

2. What does it mean to have your heart FIXED?

According to the Strong's Concordance, FIXED in this passage means to be erect, to be established in God!

Read: 2 Thessalonians 3:3

3. Who will establish you?

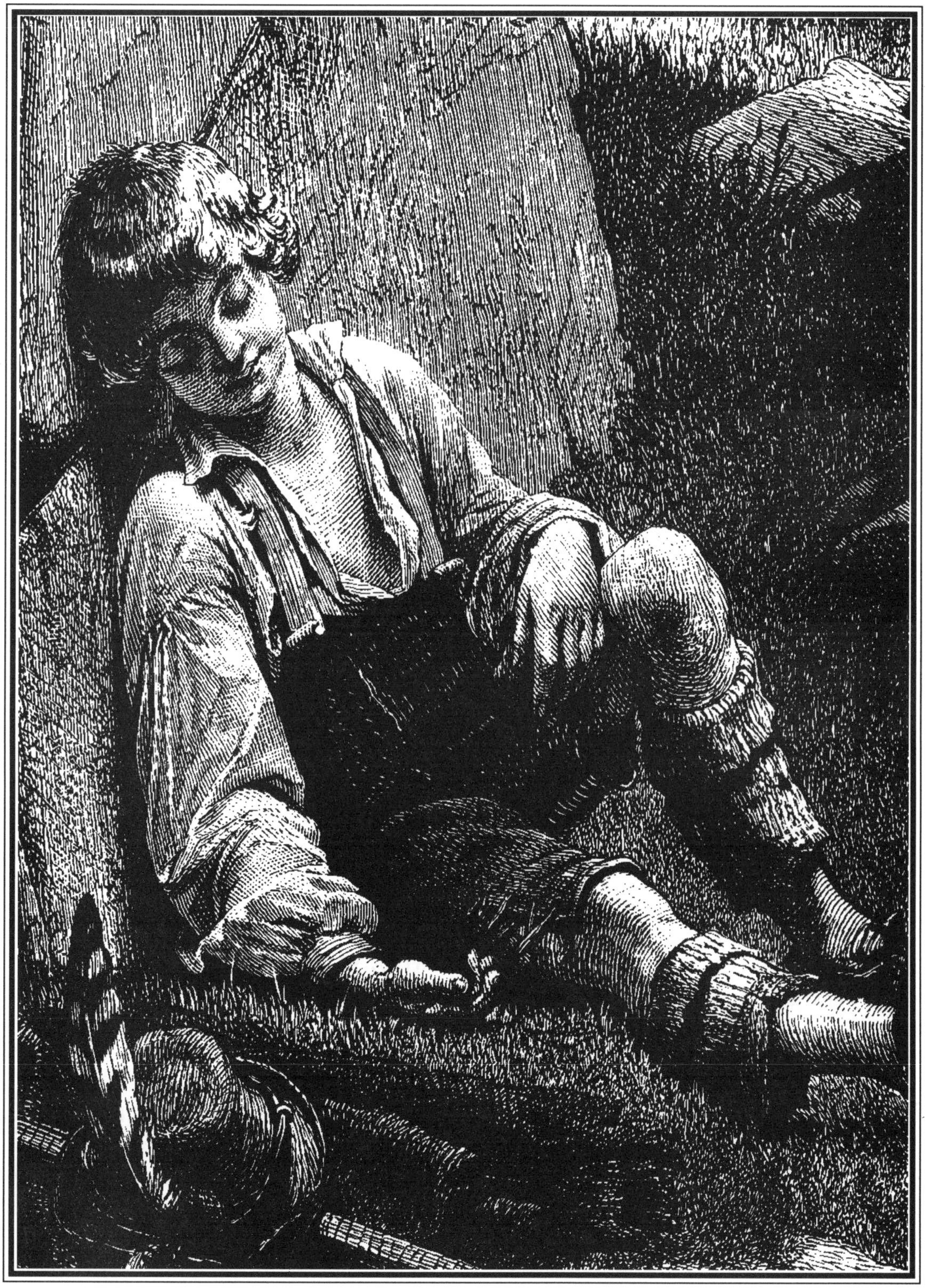

Chapter XVI

A. INDOLENCE

1. What is indolence?

   Dictionary Work: INDOLENCE

2. Write the definition below:

Another word for INDOLENCE is SLOTHFULNESS or LAZINESS.

Read: Proverbs 6:6-11

3. Complete the following commands:

    a. _____ to the ant, thou sluggard;
    b. _____ her ways, and
    c. _____ .

4. Explain what a sluggard does in this scripture:

5. Why is a good "by-law" to be an early riser in the morning?

6. What does the scripture think of sluggards?

Read: Proverbs 12:24

7. What shall the diligent do? What about the slothful?

Read: Proverbs 18:9

8. What is the "slothful in work" a brother to?

9. What does God think of those who are wasters?

Read: Proverbs 19:15

10. What shall a person who is idle suffer?

Read: Proverbs 26:13-16

11. List below the four traits of a lazy man:

_____
_____
_____
_____

B. A LAZY BOY MAKES A LAZY MAN

1. If you refuse to work hard, do you think it will be easy for you to grow up to be a hard-working man?

2. What do you think of the scripture "He who doesn't work, doesn't eat"?

Explain:

Read: 2 Thessalonians 3:10-11

3. What is a busybody?

📖   According to the Strong's the Greek word means to be busy about useless matters; doing everything that they should not do; meddlers in the business of others; prying into the domestic affairs of others. Such people are a curse to every neighborhood and a plague to every fellowship.

4. How does idleness relate to people turning into busybodies?

Read: Proverbs 14:23

5. Explain this scripture?

C. A MAN PERISHES WITHOUT A VISION

1. When a man has no purpose but to live to self, why will he perish?

2. How does a man who believes in Christ live?

3. What is a believer's vision?

Read: Proverbs 29:18

4. What happens to people who have no vision?

5. What does the scripture state we are to keep?

6. What are we as believers to keep?

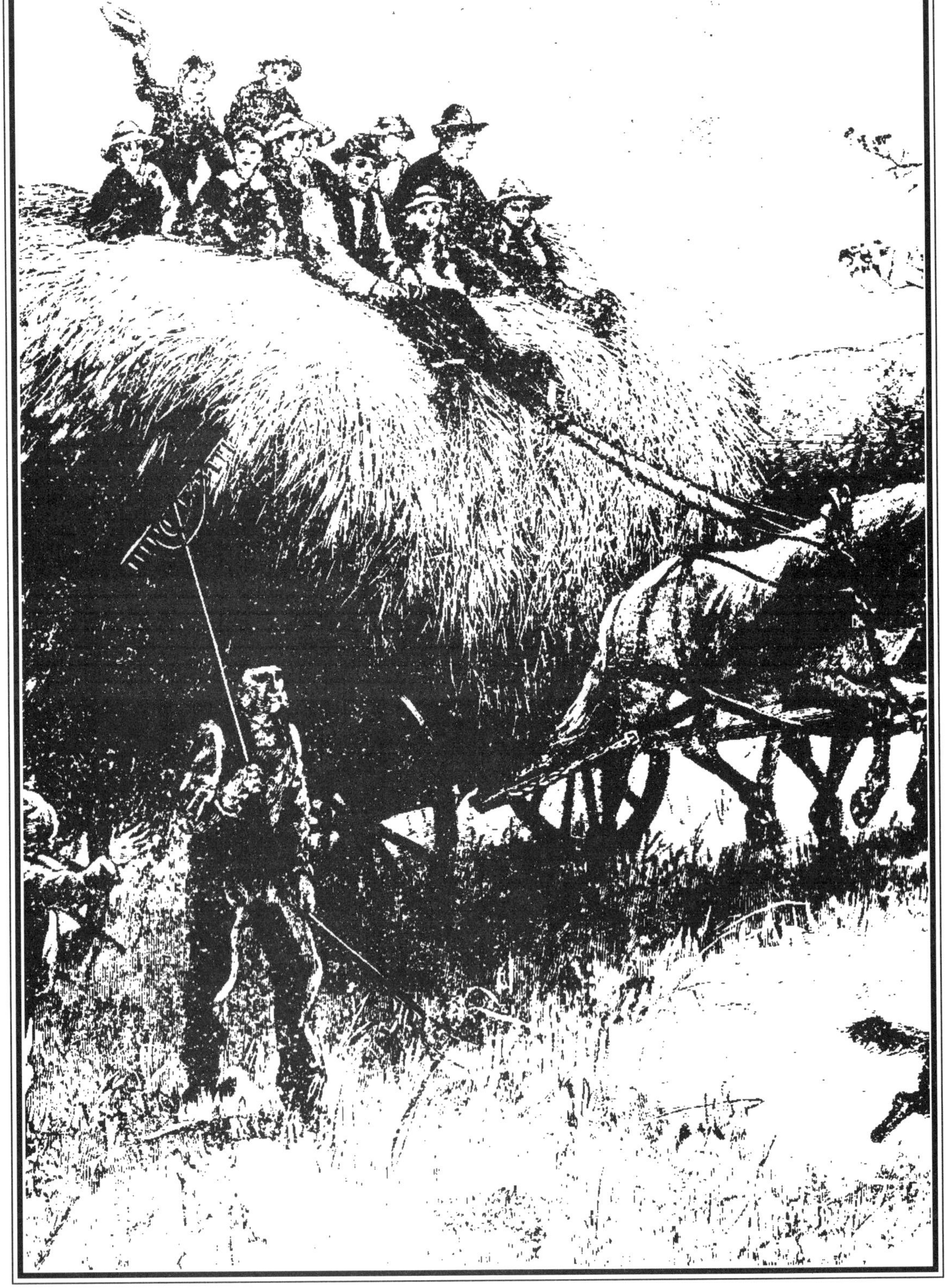

Chapter XVII

A. INDUSTRIOUSNESS

   1. What does INDUSTRIOUS mean?

Dictionary Work: INDUSTRIOUS

   2. Write the definition below:

   3. List some ways that you can be industrious in regards to your home:

Another meaning of industrious is that a person is characterized by stead attention and effort.

B. A YOUNG MAN NEEDS A USEFUL PURSUIT AND A WORTHY AIM

   1. Describe in your own words what it is to have a goal:

   2. What are some goals that you hold dear? List four:

      1.

      2.

      3.

      4.

3. Why is it important for you as a young man to have goals?

4. The Bible tells us that we should work six days and rest one. This was instituted before the law in the beginning of the world. Why did God institute this?

Read: Genesis 2:2-3

5. What did God do to the seventh day?

Read: Exodus 23:12

6. Write the scripture below:

7. Which commandment was this?

Read: Proverbs 14:4

8. What is this proverb saying?

Read: Proverbs 14:23

9. Is there profit in ALL work? Explain.

Read: Romans 12:11

10. Soon, you will have a job where you will support your family. How are you to be in business?

Read: Ephesians 4:28

11. Complete the commands below:

a. Let him that _____

b. But rather let him _____

c. That he may _____
_____

Read: 1 Thessalonians 4:11-12

12. Why are you to study to be quiet and to do your own business?

Read: 1 Timothy 5:8

13. What does God think of those who do not work and provide for their own families?

C. THE NEED FOR ORDER

1. Why is ORDER important?

📖   When one does things in an ORDERLY manner one will have a methodical and systematic arrangement. It means correctly conducted, properly arranged, or peaceable.

2. The opposite of orderly is CHAOTIC or CHAOS. Do you know what that means? Explain:

📖   According to the dictionary, the word CHAOS came from the Greek meaning of a vast abyss or chasm. It means any condition or place of total disorder or confusion.

3. What does God think of confusion?

Read: 1 Corinthians 14:33

4. Does confusion come from God? Where does it come from?

D. INDUSTRY, PERSEVERANCE & FIDELITY

1. When one is a hard worker, will he persevere until what he is working on is completed?

2. Do you persevere?

👓   Dictionary Work: PERSEVERE

3. Write the definition below:

Read: Ephesians 6:18

4. What are we to persevere in in this Scripture?

5. Why is it important to persevere in whatever we endeavor to do?

98

Chapter XVIII

A. INTEGRITY

1. What is it to have INTEGRITY? What does it mean when a person says of another, "He is a man of great integrity"?

Dictionary Work: INTEGRITY

2. Write definition below:

3. The synonym of INTEGRITY is HONESTY. How important is it to be honest?

Read: 2 Corinthians 8:21

4. Name the two in whose sight we are to provide honest things:

    a._____
    b._____

Read: Romans 12:17

5. How are we to be towards all men?

Read: Philippians 4:8

6. Why do you believe that God would have us think on honest things? What happens if we dwell on DIShonest things?

Read: 1 Peter 2:12

7. How are we to speak to those who are Gentiles? What was a "GENTILE"?

Read: Romans 13:13

8. How are we to walk?

B. CULTIVATE THE HIGHEST INTEGRITY

1. When you become involved in business, there are many opportunities to be dishonest. How important is it that even if you LOSE money, you remain HONEST?

2. Does God know when you are dishonest?

📖   The Bible tells us that there is no darkness nor any hiding place from the Lord. He is there even in the darkest place. The Scriptures also tell us in Proverbs that God hates a dishonest weight. This is an abomination to Him. We should tremble in Holy fear should we ever even be tempted with being dishonest in business! It is better to be poor and honest, than rich and dishonest!

Read: 1 Thessalonians 4:12

3. How are we to walk towards those who are in the world?

4. How are our lives an example to those who are without Christ?

Read: Hebrews 13:18

5. How would you react in a situation where you knew that being honest could hurt you? For an example, there is a story of some believers in another country who were interrogated by a certain policeman. The policeman came into their home and put a gun to their heads and said that if they said they WERE NOT Christians he wouldn't shoot them. Now all it would take would be to LIE and say they weren't Christians and they would live... What would God think of this?

The end of the story is this, that when they did not deny the Lord, the man put his gun back inside its holster and he threw his arms around the family and said, "I had to know if you were truly believers, for I, TOO, am one!"

Read: 1 Timothy 2:2

6. How do we lead a quiet and peaceable life?

Read: Proverbs 14:5

7. Complete the sentences:

   a. A faithful witness_____
   b. A false witness_____

Read: Psalm 55:23

8. Will a deceitful man live a long life?

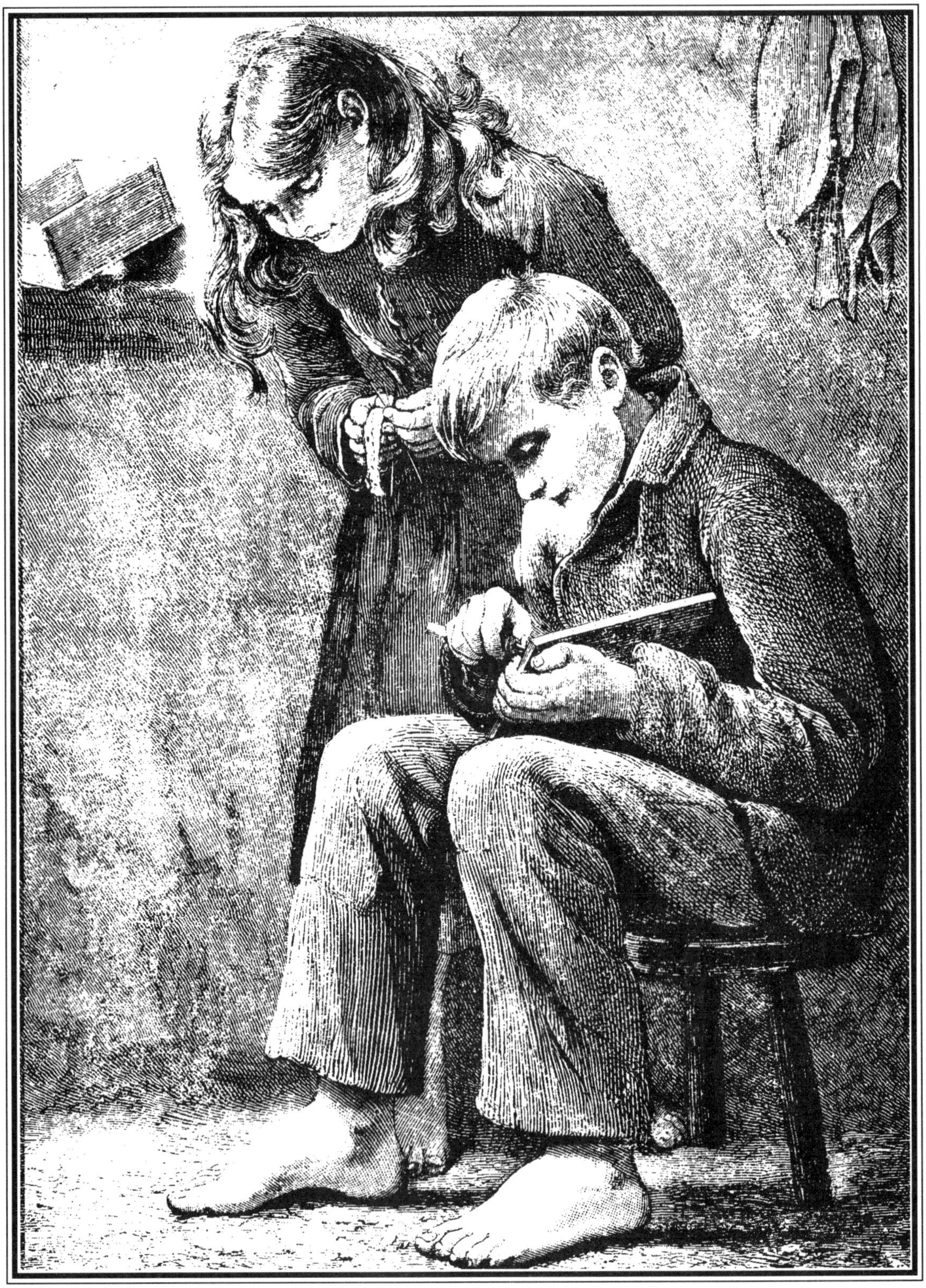

Chapter XIX

A. INFLUENCE

   1. What do you think the meaning of INFLUENCE is?

   Dictionary Work: INFLUENCE

   2. Write the definition below:

   3. Who has influenced you in your life?

   4. How has the Lord Jesus Christ influenced you?

   5. How do you influence others? Are you a good influence?

B. AN INFLUENCE NEVER DIES

   1. Describe what the Bible says about BAD INFLUENCES (company)?

   2. List below things that might be bad influences that are NOT human beings?

        a._____
        b._____
        c._____
        d._____

e._____

3. Can you ever ERASE things from your mind? If not, how important is it that we think on the things the Word tells us to think upon?

4. If you have already been influenced through worldly things what does the Bible tell us to do? How do you RENEW you mind?

Read: Romans 12:2

Another meaning for RENEW according to the Strong's Concordance is RENOVATE! To totally redo!

C. YOUR INFLUENCE UPON OTHERS FOR GOD'S PURPOSES

1. We are commanded by the Lord to go into all the world and preach the gospel. Preaching influences others. Explain how:

Read: Mark 16:15-16

   Dictionary Work: PREACH

2. Write the definition below:

3. Which definition do you think describes the Bible meaning of PREACH? Write it below again.

4. Are you to be FORCEFUL in your influence? Explain.

Read: 1 Thessalonians 2:7

5. How gentle was Paul?

6. How ought we to be towards ALL people?

Read: Acts 10:42-43

7. When the believers preached, what did they tell the people?

8. Should we preach the same thing?

Read: 2 Timothy 4:2

9 Complete the following commands:

    a. _____ the word!
    b. Be_____ in season! out of season!
    c. _____
    d._____
    e._____ with all long-suffering and doctrine!

Read: 1 Corinthians 1:18-21

10. How does the world perceive the preaching of the cross?

11. What is God's true wisdom? How do you influence others in this wisdom?

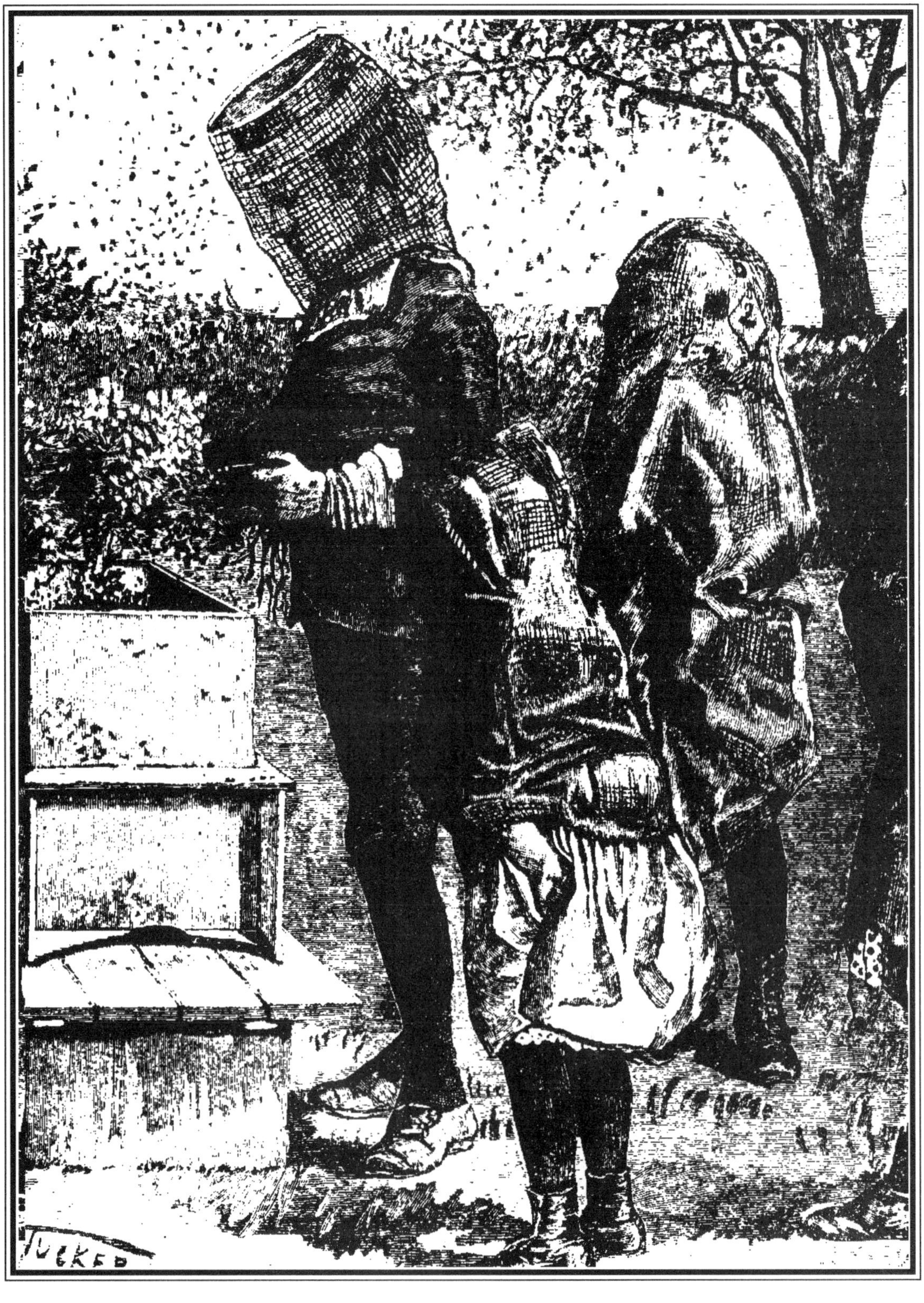
TUCKER

Chapter XX

A. CHOOSING A VOCATION

1. Write what you learned a vocation was in this chapter:

　　　Dictionary Work: VOCATION

2. Write the definition below:

3. How important is it that a man work? Can you quote some of the scriptures you studied regarding this topic?

4. Are there any vocations that you might be interested in? List some below:

　　　a._____
　　　b._____
　　　c._____
　　　d._____
　　　e._____
　　　f._____

5. If you do not have any ideas of any vocations that you might like, take time each day to read through either the encyclopedia or the dictionary. Start with A, then B and C and so forth, and when you find something that interests you, write it down. For six months make a journal. Write down and do a systematic study of topics. Then, narrow it down to a few you really think might be for you. Study your topics, and most of all, PRAY.

B. THE NEED FOR GOOD, SOUND ADVICE

1. When you are in the process of deciding what your vocation will be, you must look to those who will give you Godly counsel. Why is it important that you go to those who love the lord and not to those in the world?

Read: Proverbs 1:5

2. Complete below what a wise man will do:

    a. A wise man will:

    _____

    _____

    b. A man of understanding will:

    _____

    _____

Read: Proverbs 11:14

3. What happens when there is no counsel? What happens when there is a multitude of counselors?

Read: Proverbs 15:22

4. What will all your endeavors (purposes) come to without counsel?

5. How will you establish your plans (purposes)?

6. These scriptures tell us that you must seek counsel in all areas of your life. This also applies to your vocation. If you were going to become a veterinarian and you never learned the things you need to know, would you be able

to take care of animals?

C. THE AIM

1. What are you to aim at?

2. If you do not grow up and provide for your family, what does the Bible say you are? (Do you remember the scripture from the chapter about work?)

3. Why is it important that a man provides for his family?

D. THE KIND OF VOCATION TO SELECT

1. Your vocation will come out of the interests you hold now. List below some interests you have:

a._____
b._____
c._____
d._____
e._____
f._____

E. ALL HONEST VOCATIONS ARE HONORABLE IN GOD'S EYES

1. There are drug dealers who are millionaires and who have everything this world has to offer. Why is this not a vocation that is good for a man of Godly character? Explain in detail.

2. There are men who work hard at being garbage collectors and they may not have much money. But is it an honest profession? Would you rather be a garbage collector or a drug dealer?

Read: Proverbs 15:16

3. Why is it better to have little with the fear of the Lord?

Read: Proverbs 16:8

4. Explain the previous scripture:

F. THE BACKGROUND OF ALL VOCATIONS

1. What is the background of all vocations?

2. Who must you seek with ALL your heart, ALL your soul and ALL your mind? Whose WILL do you want to do?

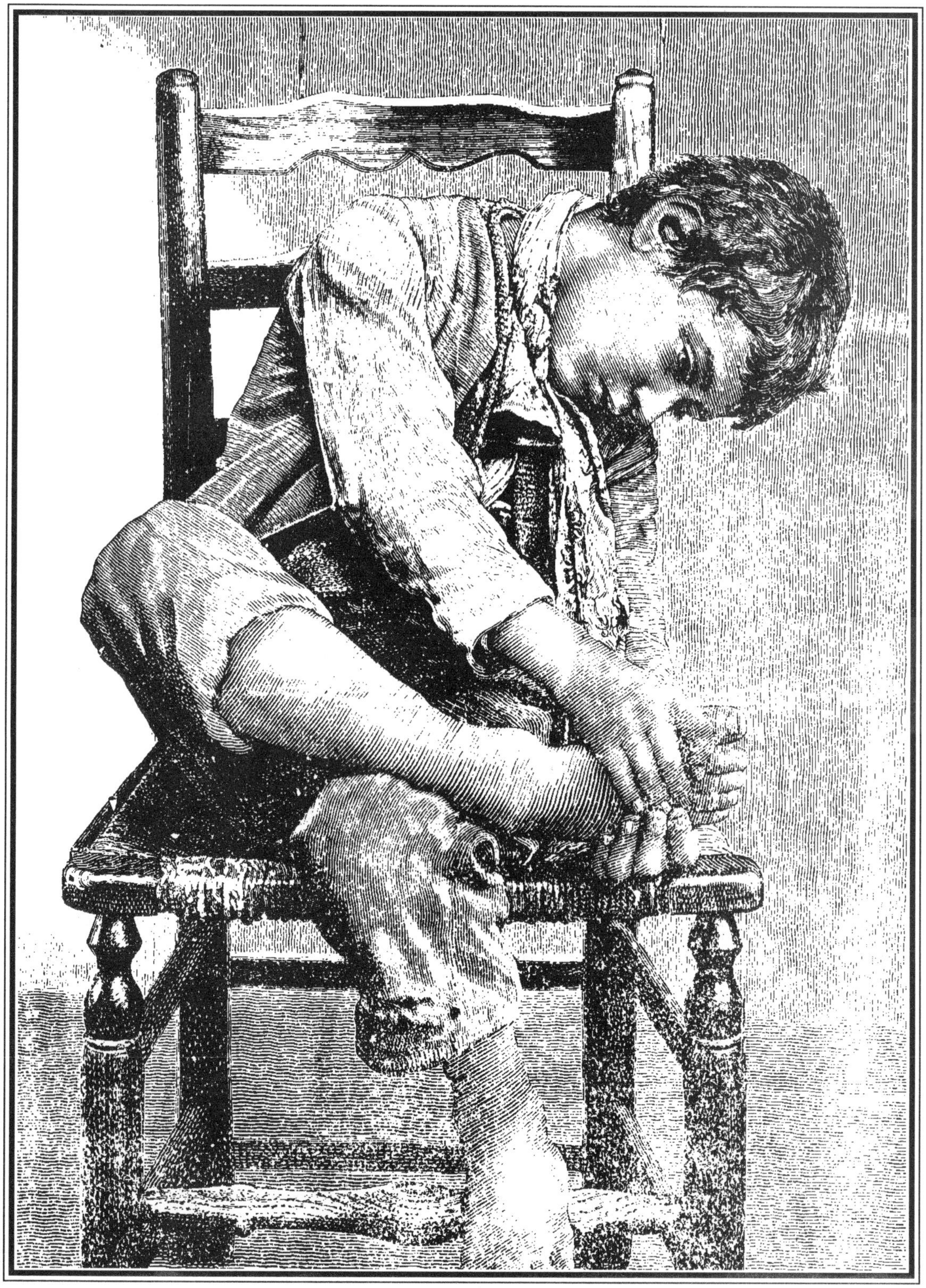

Chapter XXI

A. PLANNING YOUR WORK

1. Why is it important that you plan or make goals for your life work?

2. List below some plans that you have made regarding your vocation:

_____
_____
_____
_____
_____
_____
_____
_____
_____
_____

Read: Philippians 3:13-14

3. How can you relate this scripture in regards to your goals you have made regarding your vocation? What character trait does it portray?

Read: Psalm 119:168

4. According to this scripture, does God know our WAYS?

Read: Proverbs 3:5-6

5. What does this scripture promise in regards to our ways and our paths?

B. GETTING YOUR THOUGHTS ALIGNED TO GOD'S

1. Why is it important that we align our thoughts to the way's of God?

Read: Romans 12:2

2. Complete the following:

    a. Be not conformed to the _____.
    b. Be ye transformed by the _____.
    c. That you may prove what is that _____, _____, _____ of God.

Read: Ephesians 4:23

3. What is to be renewed in our minds?

4. When our minds are lined up with God's, will we make a mistake in our choice of vocation?

Many men at first believe that they have chosen the wrong profession, and when they seek to start another they find that they have learned many invaluable lessons from the previous. God will use everything and will allow us to go through different things in order to mold us more closely towards Him!

C. GATHER INFORMATION ABOUT YOUR VOCATION

1. It is very good to gather wisdom. God tells us true wisdom is His Word. Why must a man prepare both spiritually and physically in regards to wisdom?

2. List below sources from which you may gather information about the vocation you have chosen:

_____
_____
_____
_____
_____
_____
_____
_____

Read: Proverbs 2:2-9

3. If you first seek after God's wisdom, in verse 8, what does God promise to preserve?

4. When you go to God in prayer concerning all things, even the knowledge you learn, will HE establish your paths and your plans? Explain.

D. ONE NEEDFUL THING

1. What was the ONE NEEDFUL THING talked about in this chapter?

2. If a person is successful in business and yet they do not have God, do you think they will be truly happy?

3. Where do true Joy and Happiness come from?

Read: Mark 8:34-37

4. Answer the following questions:

   a. What will happen to a person who wishes to save his life?

   b. What will happen to those who lose their lives for Jesus' sake and the gospel's?

   c. What will a man profit if he shall gain the whole world, and lose his own soul?

   d. What shall a man give in exchange for his soul?

Read: Luke 12:16-21

5. What did this rich man do?

6. What did he say to his own soul?

7. What does God think of those who lay up treasure for themselves?

8. What does it mean to be rich towards God?

9. In your vocation, why is it important to remember this truth?

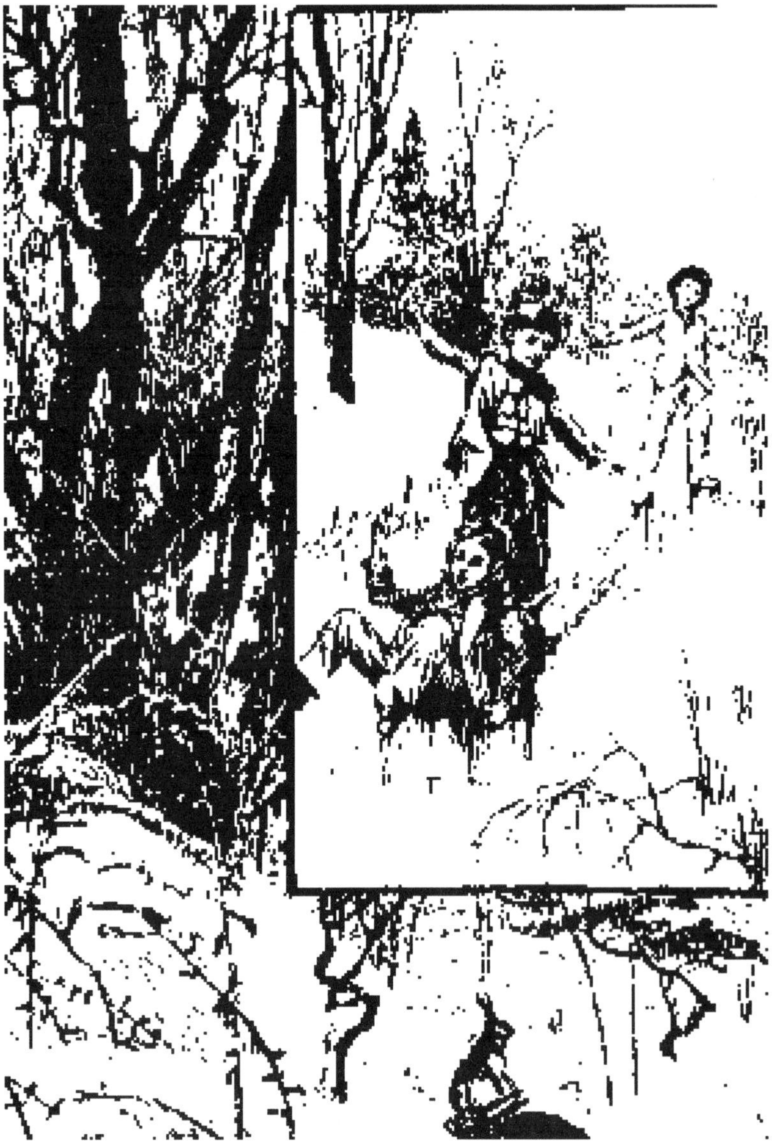

Chapter XXII

A. TRAITS OF CHARACTER IN THE WORK FORCE

   1. Why is it important to portray Godly character in your work place?

   2. Let's say that you are a boss. List below all the things that you would look for in an employee:

      a._____
      b._____
      c._____
      d._____
      e._____
      f._____
      g._____

   3. Explain how you are an ambassador for Christ. How should one representing Him be in character?

Read: Proverbs 22:1

   4. Describe what it is to have a GOOD NAME?

B. YOUR WORK NOT CARRIED TO AN EXCESS

   1. Have you ever heard of a WORKAHOLIC? What do you think that is?

2. God tells us to have self-control through His spirit. Would being a workaholic show self-control?

Read: Proverbs 23:1-3

3. What is it to be a man "given to appetite"?

4. Is gluttony a sin? Explain:

Read: Proverbs 25:16

5. How much are we to eat, according to the scripture?

Read: 1 Corinthians 9:25-27

6. What should we be in all things?

7. How are we to keep our bodies? What is it to keep them under subjection?

Read: Philippians 4:5

8. What is to be made known to all men?

👓   Dictionary Work: TEMPERANCE

9. Write the definition below:

👓 Dictionary Work: MODERATION

10. Write the definition below:

C. HAVE INITIATIVE

1. Explain what it means to "take the initiative"":

👓 Dictionary Work: INITIATIVE

2. Write the definition below:

3. Why would an employer want to hire someone with initiative?

👓 Dictionary Work: ZEAL

4. Write the definition below:

Read: Ecclesiastes 9:10

5. How are we to do all things?

6. Should we do things "half way"?

Read: 1 Corinthians 14:12

7. What are we to excel in here?

Read: Galations 4:18

8. Is it good to be zealous? Should we be zealous in all things?

Read: Revelation 3:19

9. What are we to be zealous in in this scripture?

Read: Revelation 3:14-18

10. Were these believers zealous?

11. Were they indifferent?

12. What were they? Explain what it is to be lukewarm.

13. What caused them to become this way?

14. What must you guard your own heart from?

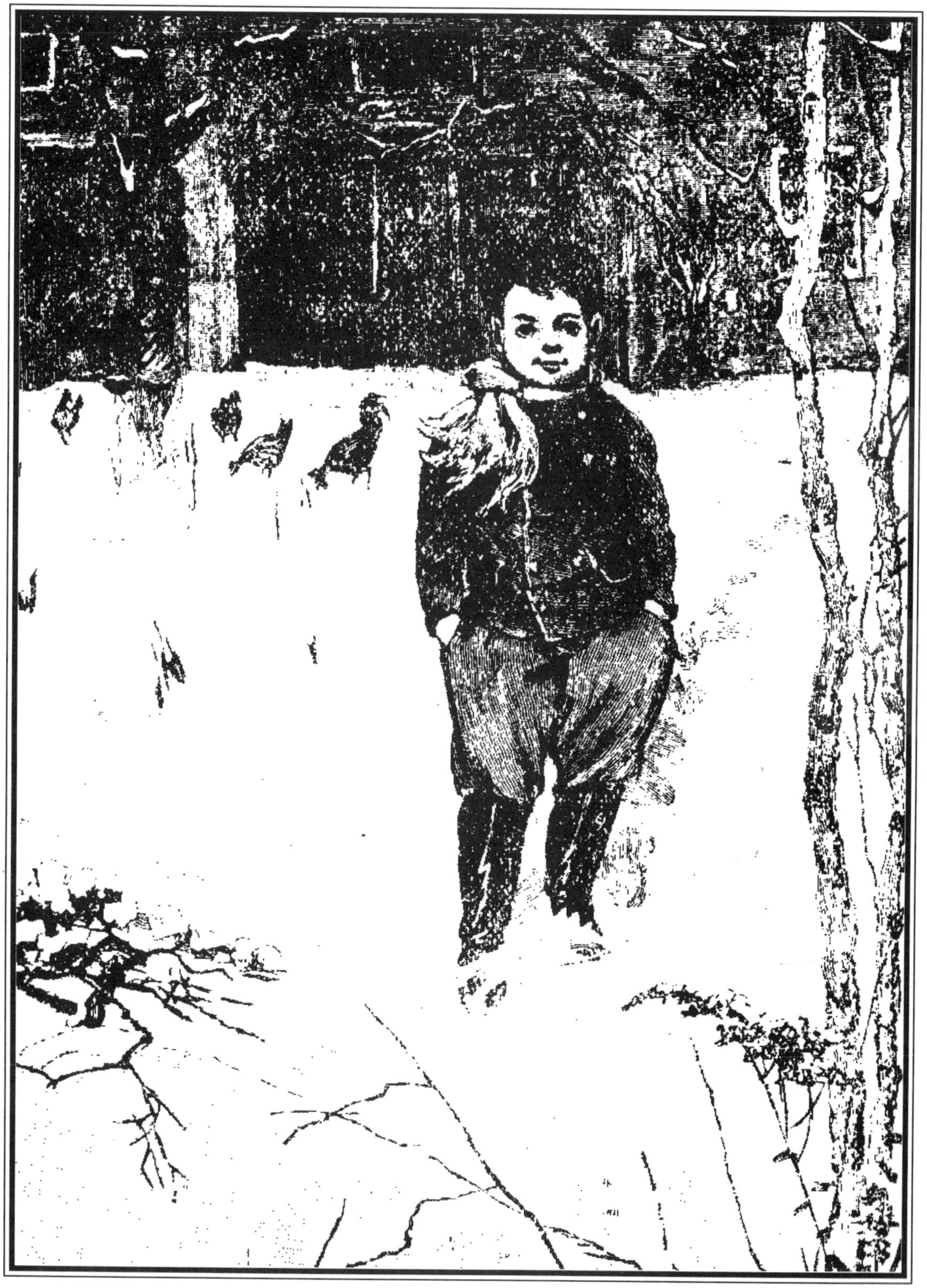

Chapter XXIII

A. YOUR JOURNEY THROUGH LIFE

1. Many people through the ages have called life a "journey". Why do you think this is so?

2. How tight can we hold onto our earthly lives? Will this body live forever? What about our spirits?

Read: Proverbs 27:1

3. Do we know what each day will bring? What does it mean when we are commanded not to boast of tomorrow?

Read: James 4:13-14

4. What is our life? Can we plan for tomorrow? What is the difference between planning and boasting in tomorrow?

Read: Hebrews 11:13

5. What did all the ones in faith before us confess in this verse?

6. What does it mean to you that we are to live here on earth as pilgrims and strangers?

Read: 1 Peter 2:11

7. What is the apostle beseeching us to do in this scripture?

8. Explain how this is telling us to not fit in with the world.

Dictionary Work: PILGRIM

9. Write the definition below:

10. How does this relate to your life?

B. THE HILLS OF DIFFICULTY

1. When one has difficulties in this life, it is usually the hand of the Lord trying to teach us something. Why do we face trials?

Read: John 15:18-20

2. In regards to this world, what are we going to find according to this scripture?

3. Will life always be easy? How does having a Godly character help you to handle the trials and tribulations of this life?

Read: Romans 8:35-39

4. The Bible says that in our tribulations, distress, persecution, famines, etc., that we are more than conquerors. Explain.

Read: James 1:12

5. How is a man blessed in this scripture?

6. In your work place you may have many temptations you must face. What will happen at the end of your temptations when you do not yield in Christ?

Read: 1 Peter 4:12-14

7. When you suffer for righteousness sake what should you be?

8. What if your employer asked you to do something that was against your beliefs, would you face unemployment rather than giving in?

C. THE ONLY RIGHT ROAD - THE NARROW WAY

Read: Matthew 7:13-15

1. Complete the following:

   a. Enter ye in at the _____.
   b. For _____ is the gate, and _____ is the way, that leads to destruction.

  c. Because _____ is the gate,
  d. And _____ is the way, which leads to life.
  e. And _____ there be that find it.

  The word NARROW in the Strong's Concordance means afflict, narrow, throng, suffer tribulation, trouble.

  The word FEW in this scripture means puny, minuscule.

  2. When the rest of the world, or your work force, chooses the world's way, whose way will you choose?

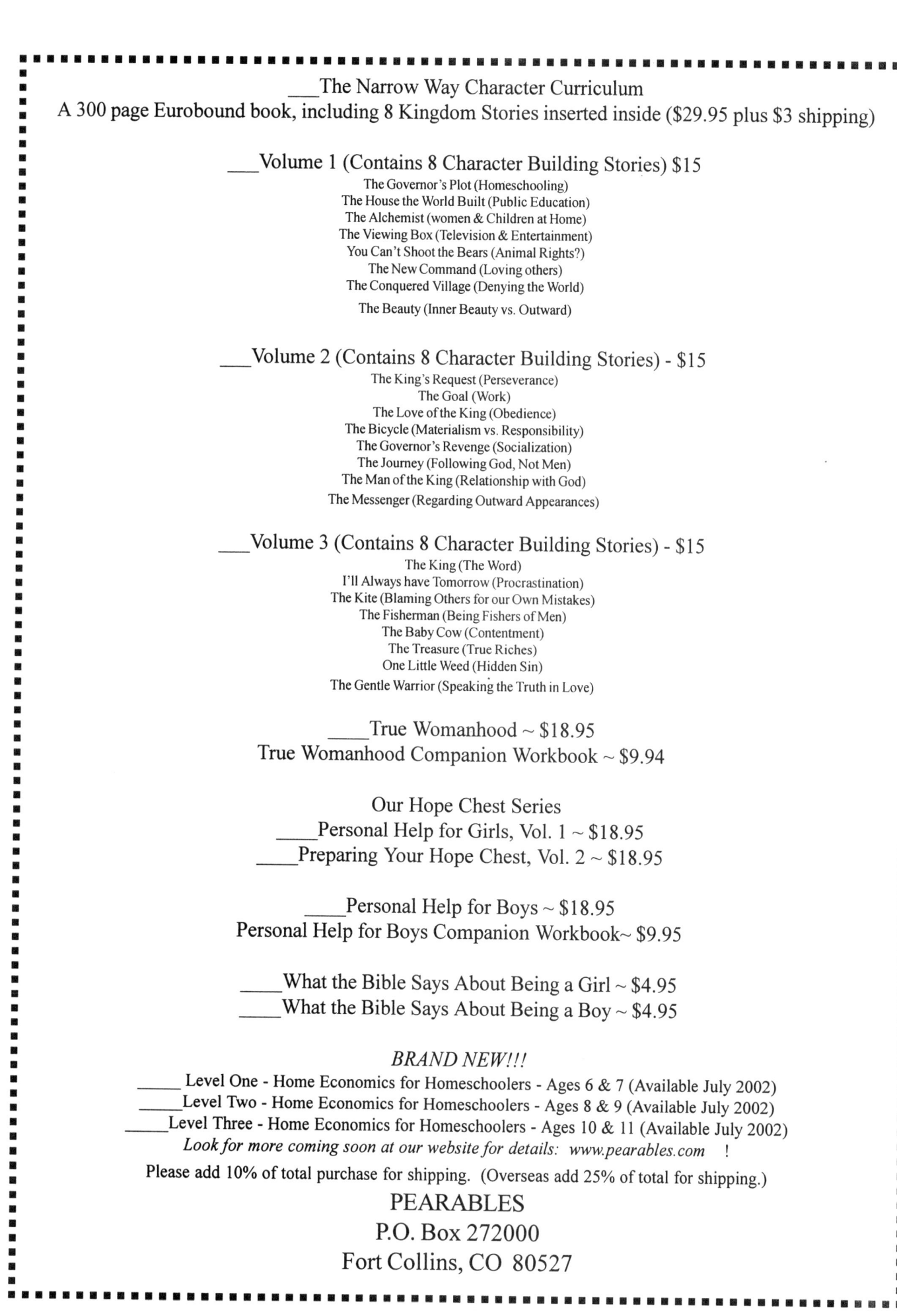

___The Narrow Way Character Curriculum
A 300 page Eurobound book, including 8 Kingdom Stories inserted inside ($29.95 plus $3 shipping)

___Volume 1 (Contains 8 Character Building Stories) $15
The Governor's Plot (Homeschooling)
The House the World Built (Public Education)
The Alchemist (women & Children at Home)
The Viewing Box (Television & Entertainment)
You Can't Shoot the Bears (Animal Rights?)
The New Command (Loving others)
The Conquered Village (Denying the World)
The Beauty (Inner Beauty vs. Outward)

___Volume 2 (Contains 8 Character Building Stories) - $15
The King's Request (Perseverance)
The Goal (Work)
The Love of the King (Obedience)
The Bicycle (Materialism vs. Responsibility)
The Governor's Revenge (Socialization)
The Journey (Following God, Not Men)
The Man of the King (Relationship with God)
The Messenger (Regarding Outward Appearances)

___Volume 3 (Contains 8 Character Building Stories) - $15
The King (The Word)
I'll Always have Tomorrow (Procrastination)
The Kite (Blaming Others for our Own Mistakes)
The Fisherman (Being Fishers of Men)
The Baby Cow (Contentment)
The Treasure (True Riches)
One Little Weed (Hidden Sin)
The Gentle Warrior (Speaking the Truth in Love)

____True Womanhood ~ $18.95
True Womanhood Companion Workbook ~ $9.94

Our Hope Chest Series
____Personal Help for Girls, Vol. 1 ~ $18.95
____Preparing Your Hope Chest, Vol. 2 ~ $18.95

____Personal Help for Boys ~ $18.95
Personal Help for Boys Companion Workbook~ $9.95

____What the Bible Says About Being a Girl ~ $4.95
____What the Bible Says About Being a Boy ~ $4.95

BRAND NEW!!!
_____Level One - Home Economics for Homeschoolers - Ages 6 & 7 (Available July 2002)
_____Level Two - Home Economics for Homeschoolers - Ages 8 & 9 (Available July 2002)
_____Level Three - Home Economics for Homeschoolers - Ages 10 & 11 (Available July 2002)
Look for more coming soon at our website for details: www.pearables.com !
Please add 10% of total purchase for shipping. (Overseas add 25% of total for shipping.)

PEARABLES
P.O. Box 272000
Fort Collins, CO 80527